The big book of sacrament time activities

jenna mitchell

D1401577

senior edition
(ages 8–11)

LOST SHEEP

When Jesus was in Jerusalem, he told the people that he would visit other groups of people in other lands. Some of these people were the Nephites. To find out what he said, cross out the letters of the first word in the second grouping of letters. The first is done for you. If you get stuck, look up John 10:16.

REMEMBER . . . REOMETHMBEERR   "O T H E R

JESUS . . . JSEHESEUPS   S h e e P

AND . . . AINO   I

ALWAYS . . . AHLWAAVYSE   h a v e ,

KEEP . . . WKHIEECRH   W h i c h

THE . . . TAHREE   A R e

COMMANDMENTS . . .

   COMNMOANDMENTTS   n o t

LIVE . . . LONFE   o f

THE . . . TTNEHIS   T h i s

GOSPEL . . . GFOSOLREDL   f o l d :

CHOOSE . . . CNTHOEQSME   T h e m

THE . . . TALNSEO   A l s o

RIGHT . . . RIGIHT   I

PRAY . . . MRRUASTY   m u s t

EVERY . . . BEKRIERNYG   B R i n g ,

DAY . . . DAANYD   a n d

AND . . . ATHENYD   T h e y

YOU . . . SYHOALUL   S h a l l

WILL . . . HWEAILLR   h e a R

BE . . . BMYE   m y

HAPPY . . . VOHAPIRCYE   V o i c e ."

SHOWING FAITH

We can show our faith in Jesus Christ by doing some very important things. Decode the message below to discover what some of these things are.

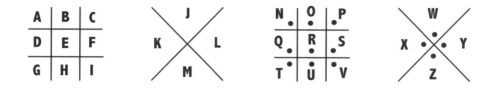

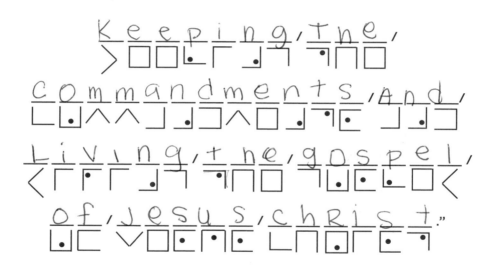

Keeping the commandments, and living the gospel of Jesus Christ."

MATTHEW 2:1–11

Use the clues below to complete the crossword puzzle. Read Matthew 2:1–12 to solve the crossword puzzle.

ACROSS:

2. King Herod demanded they tell him where Christ should be _____.

4. The visitors gave Jesus gifts of _____, frankincense, and myrrh.

6. Herod told the men they must _____ for the baby and then return to him.

8. "There came _____ from the East."

DOWN:

1. When Herod heard that Christ was born, he was

_____.

3. When they found the young child, they fell down and _____ him.

5. Where did the priests and scribes tell Herod that Christ would be born?

7. When the visitors saw the star over the baby, they

_____.

VANISHED VOWELS

The Apostle Paul gave us a very important message about the gospel of Jesus Christ. To find out what this message was, turn the letters below into words by adding vowels. If you need help, read Romans 1:16.

"F___R ___ ___M N___T ___SH___M___D ___F

TH___ G___SP___L ___F CHR___ST: F___R ___T

___S TH___ P___W___R ___F G___D ___NT___

S___LV___T___ ___N T___ ___V___RY ___N___ TH___T

B___L___ ___V___TH; T___ TH___ J___W F___RST,

___ND ___LS___ T___ TH___ GR___ ___K."

THE LAW OF TITHING

Joseph Smith inquired of the Lord concerning tithing. The Lord revealed to Joseph how much was required of the saints to give to the Church. Solve the math problems below. Find the corresponding letter from the boxes and write it on the blanks provided to find out the answer to Joseph's question.

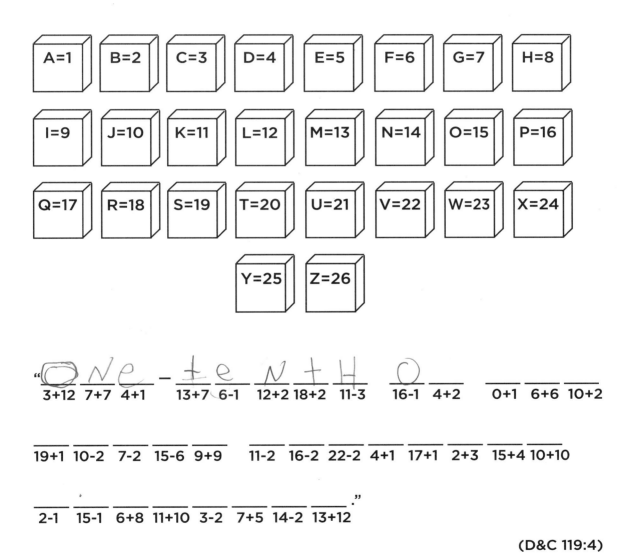

A=1	B=2	C=3	D=4	E=5	F=6	G=7	H=8
I=9	J=10	K=11	L=12	M=13	N=14	O=15	P=16
Q=17	R=18	S=19	T=20	U=21	V=22	W=23	X=24
			Y=25	Z=26			

"O N e – t e N t H O __
3+12 7+7 4+1 13+7 6-1 12+2 18+2 11-3 16-1 4+2 0+1 6+6 10+2

__ __ __ __ __ __ __ __ __ __ __ __ __
19+1 10-2 7-2 15-6 9+9 11-2 16-2 22-2 4+1 17+1 2+3 15+4 10+10

__ __ __ __ __ __ __."
2-1 15-1 6+8 11+10 3-2 7+5 14-2 13+12

(D&C 119:4)

A MIGHTY CHALLENGE

The Prophet Elijah went to a meeting with King Ahab and the prophets of Baal. Elijah wanted to show the children of Israel that these prophets were false. Elijah challenged them to show their power. To discover what he challenged them to do write the letter that comes in alphabetical order between each pair of letters. (For this puzzle, A follows Z.) You can read the story in 1 Kings 18:20–39.

___ ___   ___ ___ ___ ___   ___ ___ ___ ___
SU NP   BD ZB KM KM   CE NP VX MO

___ ___ ___ ___   ___ ___ ___ ___
EG HJ QS DF   EG QS NP LN

___ ___ ___ ___ ___ ___   ___ ___   ___ ___ ___ ___
GI DF ZB UW DF MO   SU NP   AC TV QS MO

___ ___ ___   ___ ___ ___ ___ ___ ___ ___ ___ ___.
SU GI DF   RT ZB BD QS HJ EG HJ BD DF

PICTURE SEARCH

In the picture of the Salt Lake Temple are many hidden items. See if you can find a sword, a boot, a necktie, some grapes, a chair, a table, a pear, and a pair of glasses.

NAME THAT PROPHET

Read the biographical sketch and unscramble the words taken from it. Then copy the numbered letters to the spaces with the same number to find out which prophet is described in the following paragraph.

This prophet was born on September 8, 1873. He grew up in Huntsville, Utah. He studied at the Weber Stake Academy and the University of Utah to prepare for a career in education. He later married Emma Ray Riggs in 1901 after he had completed school and served a mission. He was called as an Apostle at age 32 and was sustained as President of the Church on April 9, 1951. The first stakes were created outside of the U.S. under his administration. This prophet served in the Quorum of the Twelve for 44 years and for 19 as Church President. He died on January 18, 1970, in Salt Lake City.

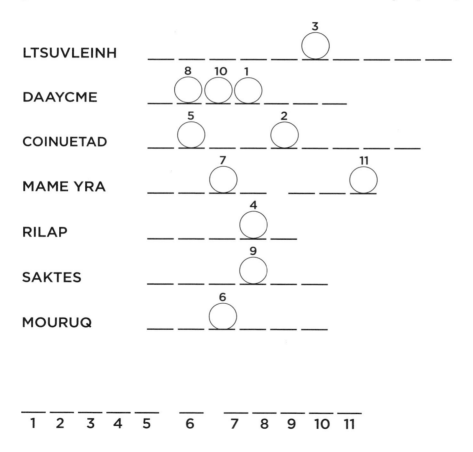

LTSUVLEINH

DAAYCME

COINUETAD

MAME YRA

RILAP

SAKTES

MOURUQ

1 2 3 4 5   6   7 8 9 10 11

FOLLOW THE PROPHET

Following the prophet will lead us to the Savior. Start with the President Hinckley's picture and follow the maze to get to the Savior.

3 NEPHI 5:13

Read 3 Nephi 5:13. Then find the words from the scripture in the word search.

```
L  U  D  B  V  A  L  E  D  V  V  G  R  Z  E
D  O  V  R  F  B  L  L  O  A  X  N  W  Y  D
S  F  Y  K  O  P  E  R  G  N  V  I  L  P  U
A  E  Q  J  I  W  S  H  C  Z  Z  T  A  Y  L
Y  D  E  C  L  A  R  E  O  K  J  S  T  M  H
C  M  S  S  Z  J  W  F  U  L  I  A  G  O  K
X  I  O  P  N  A  B  F  W  R  D  L  F  G  D
D  V  H  V  M  E  F  I  L  Y  N  R  N  G  C
G  D  K  R  Z  F  T  E  Z  Z  K  E  R  N  A
K  B  G  M  W  C  A  L  F  P  J  V  P  N  L
A  G  D  A  E  E  O  P  M  J  U  E  O  V  L
V  J  M  J  N  L  Y  D  C  L  O  S  P  N  E
A  A  Y  V  B  D  F  Q  F  P  E  S  J  M  D
G  A  B  B  U  S  G  P  L  Z  Z  H  L  U  T
R  K  X  U  U  O  C  E  N  Y  L  V  J  K  K
```

BEHOLD   CALLED   DECLARE

DISCIPLE   EVERLASTING   GOD

LIFE   PEOPLE   WORD

ARE YOU HUMBLE?

Being humble means we are meek and teachable. If we are humble, we recognize our dependency on God and we value other people. Read each scripture below. Then match it with the blessing it teaches that we receive by being humble.

The Lord will lift us up.

We shall see and know the Lord.

We can be great in the kingdom of Heaven.

We can learn wisdom and our eyes will be opened.

The Lord will guide us and answer our prayers.

We can be made strong and receive knowledge.

D&C 136:32

James 4:10

D&C 112:10

Matthew 18:4

D&C 1:28

D&C 67:10

GREAT GIFTS

King Benjamin gave Mosiah the brass plates, the Liahona, and one more item before he died. To find out what this was, follow the clues and put the correct letters in the blanks. (See Mosiah 1:16 for help.)

_____ 1. You'll find me once in NOSE and twice in HAPPINESS.

_____ 2. You'll find me in WATER but not in SPRITE or ORANGE JUICE.

_____ 3. I'm once in ON and once in OFF.

_____ 4. I'm a consonant in RIDDLE but not in FIDDLE.

_____ 5. I'm a consonant in DEEP but not in CREEP.

_____ 6. I'm a vowel in OREGON but not in DELAWARE.

_____ 7. Look for me in FOOD and FUN.

_____ 8. I'm once in ALMOND and twice in VANILLA.

_____ 9. You'll find me once in APPLE, three times in BANANA.

_____ 10. I'm a consonant in BLACK but not in SLACK.

_____ 11. You'll find me in HAT but not in SHIRT.

_____ 12. You'll find I'm in NAIL but not in FAIL.

____ ____ ____ ____ ____   ____ ____   ____ ____ ____ ____ ____

COMMON STORIES

Some things Heavenly Father has taught us through stories in the Bible are also taught to us through the Book of Mormon. First unscramble the bold letters at the top of the columns to spell a character's name from the Bible. Place the unscrambled letters in the correct order in the top of the empty boxes. Take the columns that appear under each scrambled letter and write them under that same letter in the empty columns. Then read left to right to see what the Book of Mormon and Bible character have in common.

P	H	N	E	E	S	T
PUT T NIES REP	O AND ENT.	BEARING G THE	FOR TELLIN	WERE IMO TO	AND THEIR CHIEF	ABINADI TEST RULERS

Mosiah 17:2–5
Acts 7:51–60

PRAYER POWER

Read the scripture below. Then read up, down, across, backwards, and diagonally to find the word "prayer" 13 times in the letter square.

"And the prayers of the faithful shall be heard, and all those who
have dwindled in unbelief shall not be forgotten." (2 Nephi 26:15)

```
P R A Y E R P R A R
R P R P R A Y E R E
A P E R Y P Y Y E Y
Y R E Y A R P A Y A
E A R P E A R R R R
R Y R Y A Y E P E P
P E A Y P E R E Y A
R R E Y A R P Y A E
P A R P R E Y A R P
P R A Y E R E R P A
```

ADAM AND EVE

Complete this dot-to-dot to see the picture of our first parents.

THE STORY OF DANIEL

To find the word that is missing from each sentence follow the arrows on the next page. For help, see Daniel 6.

1. King Darius made Daniel one of three _____.

2. Because they were jealous, the other presidents and princes sought to find _____ in Daniel.

3. They convinced Darius to sign a _____ that no man should pray to God.

4. But Daniel defied the decree and prayed _____ times a day.

5. Daniel was caught _____ God.

6. He was thrown into a den of _____.

7. The king was worried about Daniel and _____ for him.

8. When the king arrived at the lions' den the next day, Daniel was still _____.

9. The Lord saved Daniel because of his _____ and sent angels to shut the lion's mouths.

10. The king was _____ that Daniel was alive.

11. King Darius decreed that the God of Daniel should be _____ by all his people.

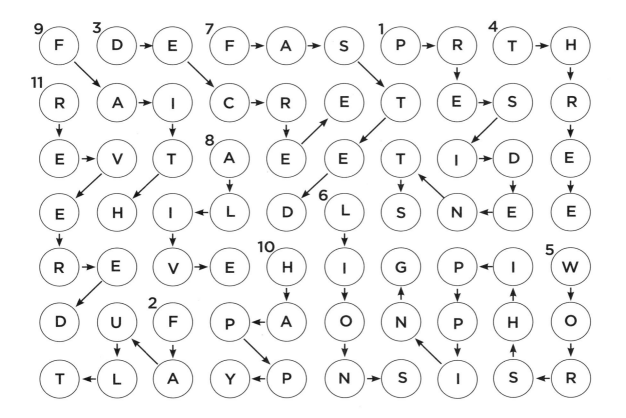

ABRAHAM'S TEST

Abraham was told to sacrifice Isaac, his only son, on an altar. Both Abraham and Isaac were going to obey the will of God, but at the last moment, an angel stopped Abraham. To find out what blessing Abraham received for his obedience, follow the path through the maze that makes a sentence.

SPECIAL CONNECTIONS

Do you know whom these clues are talking about? If you don't, use the scripture references to help. Write the answers in the blanks, and then use the numbered letters to solve the puzzle at the end.

1. This prophet confronted the wicked man Sherem, who sought to turn the people against Christ (Jacob 7:3).

2. A carpenter who was Jesus' earthly father (Matthew 1:16).
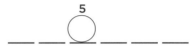

3. This prophet had a son named Orihah who became king of the Jaredites (Ether 6:27).

4. This man became a father in his old age and named his son John (Luke 1:13).

5. This man had a son named Joseph and made him a coat of many colors. He used to be called Jacob (Genesis 37:3).

6. This man prayed for his people and took his family into the wilderness when the prophets foretold the destruction of Jerusalem (1 Nephi 1:5).
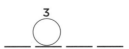

These men were all scripture F __ T __ __ __ __ .
                                 1   2 3 4 5

A BALL OF CURIOUS WORKMANSHIP

When Lehi woke up one morning to get ready to leave on a journey, he found a ball outside his tent. The ball told him which way to go into the wilderness. It was called the Liahona. See if you can draw the Liahona on the next page.

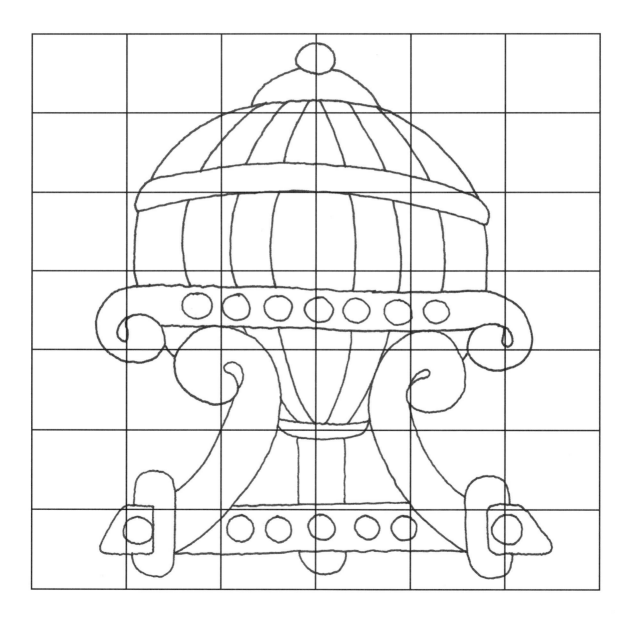

1 NEPHI 1:1

Decode the scripture below. Then read 1 Nephi 1:1.

A	B	C	D	E	F	G	H	I	J	K	L	M	N	O	P	Q	R	S	T
								14		16		6					13		8

U	V	W	X	Y	Z

"I, NEPHI, HAVING BEEN

BORN OF GOODLY

PARENTS, THEREFORE I

WAS TAUGHT SOMEWHAT

IN ALL THE LEARNING

OF MY FATHER."

REFERENCE RACE

To find what scripture these words belong to, first find them in the word search. Then find the hidden scripture reference using the first unused letters.

```
I   S   E   C   S   H   O   N   D   N   D   E   P   H   I
F   N   I   V   A   S   E   S   L   I   E   V   E   N   T
E   E   D   N   N   A   A   R   D   A   L   W   V   A   X
E   G   D   U   B   L   I   P   Y   V   B   S   N   B   W
U   S   W   G   S   E   V   K   T   U   V   O   W   J   G
Y   K   J   O   H   T   D   T   Y   K   E   B   R   T   T
Z   H   L   T   T   E   R   C   A   U   S   E   A   L   I
P   E   O   P   L   E   M   I   N   E   P   H   I   Q   G
I   B   G   Z   Q   B   P   A   O   D   A   A   T   M   W
N   D   X   J   K   V   A   P   C   U   N   A   D   A   Z
Y   L   W   M   R   V   G   S   A   D   S   B   D   T   G
```

AND	CAME	CAUSE
DID	HANDS	INDUSTRIOUS
LABOR	NEPHI	PASS
PEOPLE	THEIR	

__ __ __ __ __ / __ __ __ __ __ / __ __ __ __ :

__ __ __ __ __ __ __ __ __

GREAT MEN

Unscramble the names from the scriptures below. Then write each numbered letter in the box with the same number in the sentence at the bottom of the page.

PIHNE   ⁸◯ __ ⁹◯ __ __

MALA   __ __ ⁷◯ __

NABIANDI   __ ¹◯ __ __ __ __ __

RMINOO   __ ³◯ ⁶◯ ⁴◯ __ __

HANMAEL   ¹⁰◯ ¹¹◯ __ __ ⁵◯ __ __

MAOHIS   __ ²◯ ¹²◯ __ __ __

These men are:

__ __ __ K __ F __ __ __ __ __ __
1   2   3   4   5   3   6   7   2   8

__ __ __ __ __ __ T __
9   6   3   9   10   11   12

BLESSINGS OF FAITH

Cross out all the boxes that contain X, J, M, P, Q, S, or Y. Write the unused letters in order from left to right in the spaces below to find out what reward we have been promised if we remain faithful to the gospel.

X	J	B	M	E	P	S	Q	T	H	S	O	X	U	Y
P	F	Y	A	I	J	T	S	H	Q	F	U	Y	L	S
U	N	P	T	Q	O	M	J	D	P	E	Y	A	T	H
X	J	A	M	N	P	D	Q	J	I	P	Q	W	X	I
Q	L	X	S	L	M	J	G	X	I	S	V	M	J	E
X	S	M	Q	S	P	J	S	J	Y	T	Q	H	E	M
J	M	E	Y	Y	A	P	Q	X	C	P	M	R	J	O
Y	W	S	J	N	P	J	O	X	M	Y	F	Y	S	X
P	S	L	M	Q	I	Y	S	P	F	J	X	S	E	P

"__ __ __ __ __ __ __ __ __ __ __ __ __ __

__ __ __ __ __ __ , __ __ __ __

__ __ __ __ __ __ __ __ __ __ __

__ __ __ __ __ __ __ __ __."

(Revelation 2:10)

THE BROTHER OF JARED

The brother of Jared needed to take many things with him to get to the promised land. The most important thing he took with him was a belief in Jesus Christ. To find out what this is called, put the name of each picture in the matching line of the acrostic puzzle. The shaded area will reveal the answer.

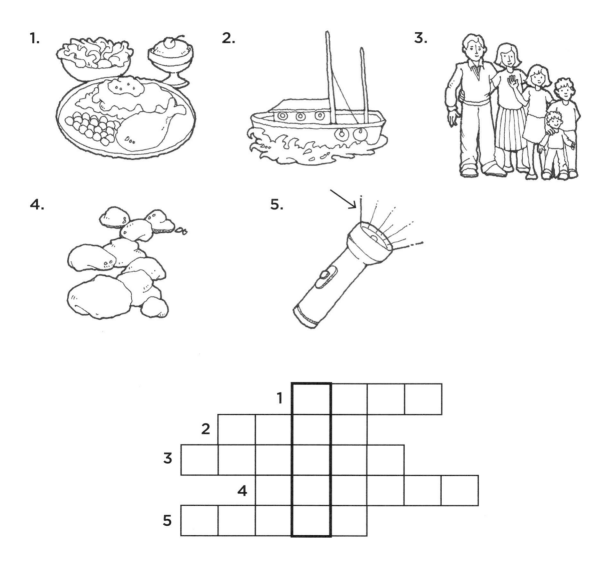

THE WORD OF GOD

Can you guess what hymn these words are from? To find out, find these words in the word search and then write the unused letters in the blanks in order until every blank has been used.

```
T  S  N  E  V  A  E  H  O  L  D  E  N
S  U  B  L  I  M  E  H  E  I  I  R  O
N  T  S  T  H  G  I  R  B  N  R  R  O
D  Y  R  T  D  P  O  G  E  E  O  E  Q
L  L  F  O  S  O  U  D  P  P  N  N  Y
W  E  C  D  N  I  R  U  E  H  C  O  O
Z  F  I  G  D  G  M  R  S  I  T  I  J
C  A  Q  E  Z  N  I  W  O  R  D  S  U
H  S  D  Z  Y  L  H  T  J  J  R  I  Y
D  A  R  K  N  E  S  S  E  Z  X  V  D
```

AID	BRIGHT	DARKNESS
GOD	GUIDE	HEAVENS
IRON	MISTS	NEPHI
OLDEN	PERIL	ROD
SAFELY	STRONG	SUBLIME
TIS	VISION	WORD

___ ___ ___

STRIPLING WARRIORS

Helaman's stripling warriors were very young and inexperienced, yet they fought without fear and with miraculous strength. Not one of them died in battle. Beginning with column #1, go down each column until you come to a dot. Copy the row's letter onto the first blank. Continue in this way for each column to find out why the stripling warriors were protected from death. See Alma 53:21 and 57:21 for help.

	1	2	3	4	5	6	7	8	9	10	11	12	13	14	15	16	17	18	19	20
A		●					●						●							
B																	●			
C				●																
D								●												●
E									●								●			
G			●																	
H			●																	
K														●						
L													●							
M					●	●		●												
N							●		●											
O				●												●			●	
R																		●		
S											●									
T	●		●							●										
U		●																		
W												●						●		
X																				
Y																	●			

"They had been ___ ___ ___ ___ ___ ___ to keep the

___ ___ ___ ___ ___ ___ ___ ___ ___ ___ ___ of God and to

___ ___ ___ ___ uprightly before him. . . . Yea, and they did ___ ___ ___ ___

and observe to perform every ___ ___ ___ ___ of command with exactness."

PARTING THE RED SEA

Complete this dot-to-dot to see the picture of Moses.

WHICH PROPHET AM I?

Read the biographical sketch below. Then unscramble the words taken from the sketch. Copy the letter in the numbered square to the spaces with the same number to find out who this prophet is.

This prophet was born on November 13, 1838, in Far West, Missouri. He was the son of Hyrum Smith, who was martyred along with the Prophet Joseph Smith in 1844. In 1848, this prophet and his mother, Mary, traveled to Utah and settled in Salt Lake City. After she died, he began a life of service in the Church. In addition, he served in Utah's territorial legislature and then later became President of the Church in 1901. This prophet brought a better appreciation of Church history to the members. He also developed Church missionary and educational systems, directed the construction of a new headquarters, and served numerous missions. He served 17 years as Church President and died on November 19, 1918.

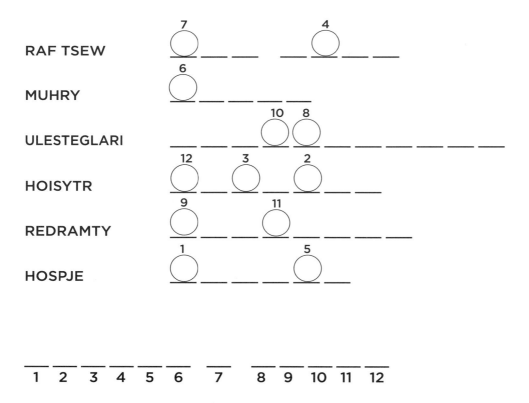

RAF TSEW

MUHRY

ULESTEGLARI

HOISYTR

REDRAMTY

HOSPJE

___ ___ ___ ___ ___ ___ ___   ___ ___ ___ ___ ___
 1   2   3   4   5   6   7   8   9 10 11 12

GEORGE ALBERT SMITH

George Albert Smith was prophet of the Church from 1945 to 1957. To hear some of his teachings, try to decode his quote by figuring out which letters correspond to which numbers.

A	B	C	D	E	F	G	H	I	J	K	L	M	N	O	P	Q	R	S	T
				21							1		7					8	17

U	V	W	X	Y	Z
		16			

"___ W___L__ N_T _E
 6   16 11 12 1 26   7 11 17   5 21

___ _N_ _ENE__ T_ _N_
15 7   21 7 21 4 9   17 11   15 7 9

L___N_ S__L."
1 6 22 6 7 2   8 11 12 1

PICTURE SEARCH

In the picture of Ammon with King Lamoni's sheep are many hidden items. Find a piece of pie, a teddy bear, a spoon, a fork, an ice cream cone, an ax, and a hanger.

13TH ARTICLE OF FAITH

Use your knowledge of the Articles of Faith to complete the crossword. If you need help, look it up in your scriptures! (You can find the Articles of Faith at the end of the Pearl of Great Price.)

ACROSS:

4. "We believe in doing _____ to all men."
5. Another word for beauty.
7. The 6th to last word.
9. "We _____ all things." (7 letters)

DOWN:

1. Whose admonition do we follow?
2. "We hope to _____ all things."
3. "We _____ all things." (4 letters)
6. Another word for having high standards. It is mentioned twice.
8. Another word for being truthful.

THE ARMOR OF GOD

Complete the dot-to-dot to see what an ancient sword and shield of the Nephites might have looked like.

HIDDEN HYMNS

Can you guess which hymn these words belong to? Find them in the word search and then read the unused letters to find out!

```
C A G L O R Y Y R O T S L P
L E D T O S L E R V E F R S
O P W I T N E S S I B O K E
C O N F E S S I N G C N I S
E V S V S E D T R L O A N I
L V A L D V R R A N N M G A
T E R B Z I R I A N W E X R
H X Q E U Q M X J W A H D P
G B I M S U G H B M R X L M
X M P U S T W V J V D O V N
O H Q P B X C V O W S V F N
```

CONFESSING   **FORWARD**   **GLORY**
HEAVENLY   **KING**   **NAME**
ONWARD   **PRAISES**   **PROCLAIM**
SERVE   **STORY**   **TRIUMPH**
WITNESS

__ __ __ __ __ __   __ __   __ __ __ __ __

NEPHI'S WARNING

Nephi, the son of Helaman, was a very righteous man. He prophesied to the Nephites that if they didn't repent God would destroy them. Decode the message below to find out what happened to the Nephites.

Change all D's to A's   Change all C's to N's
Change all R's to C's   Change all S's to O's
Change all P's to D's   Change all I's to P's
Change all Q's to E's   Change all U's to R's
Change all E's to G's   Change all Y's to S's
Change all X's to H's   Change all F's to T's
Change all B's to I's   Change all G's to U's
Change all Z's to L's   Change all H's to W's
Change all A's to M's   Change all K's to Y's

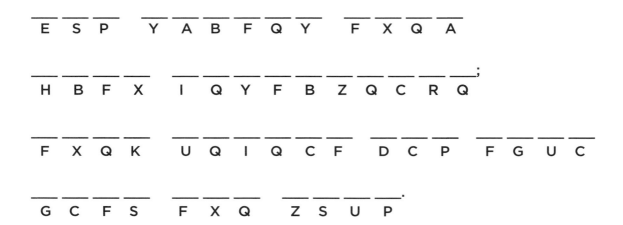

E S P   Y A B F Q Y   F X Q A

H B F X   I Q Y F B Z Q C R Q ;

F X Q K   U Q I Q C F   D C P   F G U C

G C F S   F X Q   Z S U P .

THE HOUSE OF THE LORD

Draw the other half of the church building. Remember, you only need to have a steeple on one side!

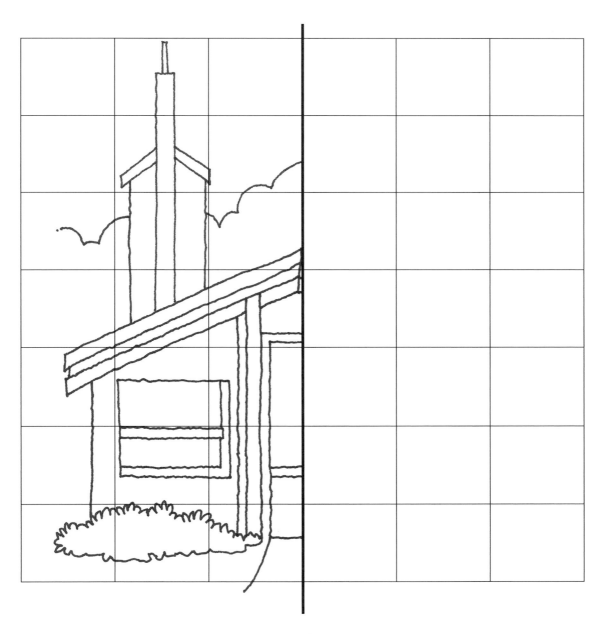

ALL MIXED UP!

The names of some of the books of the Old Testament are listed below, but they are hard to read. To unscramble the letters in each group, start at the arrow pointing IN and connect the letters to spell a book in the Old Testament, ending at the arrow pointing OUT. Some letters will not be used. The first one is done for you. Use the table of contents page in your Bible if you need help.

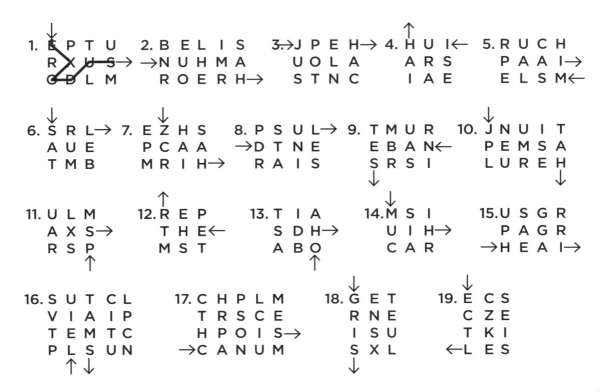

TRUE OR FALSE

For each of the statements decide which are true and which are false. Check the appropriate column for each one. Then write the number for each TRUE statement in the spaces at the bottom in ALPHABETICAL order. For example, if #2 statement is the first true statement, write the number 2 in the letter A blank. If #5 is the next true statement, write the number 5 in the letter B blank and so on. Then read each scripture about the sacrament.

T   F

☐   ☐   1. I can play with my toys during the sacrament.

☐   ☐   2. I should be reverent and respectful during the sacrament.

☐   ☐   3. The sacrament reminds us of our baptism.

☐   ☐   4. The sacrament is to help us remember the atonement of Jesus Christ.

☐   ☐   5. I can read the scriptures during the sacrament.

☐   ☐   6. During the sacrament I should think about what will be on T.V. when I get home from Church.

☐   ☐   7. The sacrament helps me be closer to Jesus.

☐   ☐   8. The bread and water are symbols.

☐   ☐   9. I should eat treats during the sacrament.

☐   ☐   10. I don't have to listen to the sacrament prayers.

Moroni ___ : ___   Moroni ___ : ___   3 Nephi 1___ : ___
      C   B   D   A   F   E

WHO AM I?

What message do we get from the following scriptures: 1 Nephi 17:36, 1 Nephi 11:17, and D&C 50:41? Read them and then color in all the boxes with an "X" to reveal the answer.

I am a . . .

X	X	X	R	X	D	X	M	X	X	X	Z	X	C	K	L	X	X	I
X	B	N	A	X	F	X	K	C	X	T	M	X	Y	W	Q	X	A	X
X	W	S	H	X	X	X	R	H	X	B	V	X	R	E	U	X	O	X
X	A	T	M	X	V	X	G	Z	X	I	M	X	C	T	H	X	P	X
X	X	X	R	X	N	X	S	X	X	X	O	X	X	X	L	X	X	I
U	I	K	H	K	P	G	M	B	E	Y	I	H	L	S	B	S	E	R
I	P	I	H	K	B	V	X	X	X	B	X	X	X	S	A	Y	U	C
M	O	I	Q	S	R	T	X	K	X	L	X	K	G	J	G	B	N	M
N	C	V	Z	O	U	I	X	E	X	M	X	X	A	Q	W	L	K	S
A	Z	F	O	A	F	P	X	S	X	A	X	F	I	S	E	Q	O	W
S	E	W	L	W	G	R	X	X	X	Q	X	M	O	D	A	H	I	P
D	W	H	J	Q	H	N	F	D	A	P	T	K	P	T	W	N	B	C
G	O	J	H	X	X	X	B	T	X	X	X	H	X	X	J	S	G	V
H	J	K	H	X	K	M	N	T	X	I	X	I	X	U	X	R	M	N
B	P	T	E	X	I	X	X	F	X	U	X	J	X	O	X	K	T	J
V	U	Y	R	X	O	X	Z	S	X	Z	X	K	X	S	X	J	H	O
N	K	I	T	X	X	X	C	V	X	X	X	I	X	X	D	F	E	P

A PROCLAMATION TO THE WORLD

What do we need to have a successful family? Solve the code to find out. (See "The Proclamation to the World," <u>Ensign,</u> Nov. 1995, 102.)

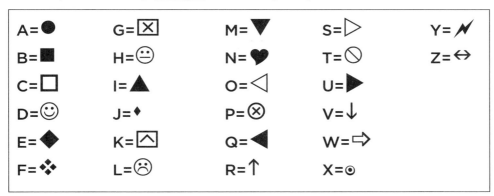

"Successful marriages and __ __ __ __ __ __ __ __ __ are established

and maintained on principles of __ __ __ __ __,

and __ __ __ __ __ __ __ __ __ recreational activities."

THE FIRST ARTICLE OF FAITH

Find the words listed from the first Article of Faith in the word search.

```
T  S  O  H  G  Y  L  O  H  Z  R  B  J
E  A  O  Y  A  H  W  A  U  E  H  E  L
V  V  W  C  J  I  D  Z  H  M  S  K  A
H  C  E  S  T  S  C  T  D  U  A  U  N
U  A  O  I  V  F  A  D  S  E  T  S  R
I  N  Z  W  L  F  N  C  T  P  X  B  E
D  M  J  P  F  E  H  O  H  K  H  A  T
D  R  F  K  U  R  B  J  J  N  V  K  E
G  C  W  F  I  Y  U  R  G  J  D  R  W
L  E  T  S  H  M  A  N  D  O  M  T  O
D  H  T  F  V  Q  I  X  S  N  D  E  F
```

AND	BELIEVE	ETERNAL
FATHER	GOD	HIS
HOLY GHOST	JESUS CHRIST	SON

A QUOTE BY A PROPHET

Follow the path that makes a sentence. You will uncover a quote by President Howard W. Hunter.

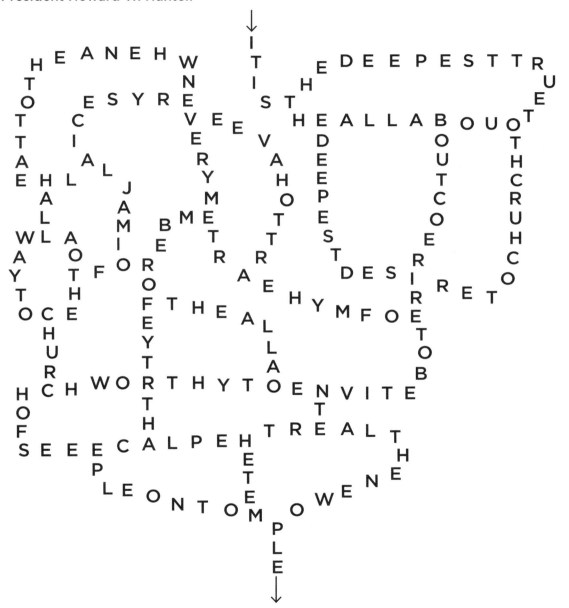

POWERFUL PROTECTION

How can we protect ourselves from temptation and evil? Use the table below to figure out which letter belongs on each line to discover the answer.

	1	2	3	4	5	6	7	8
A	Q	P	M	D	U	T	C	R
B	G	R	N	P	O	F	K	E
C	T	I	J	U	Y	S	B	H
D	X	M	H	B	L	N	V	A
E	I	L	I	S	T	F	G	D

___ ___ ___   ___ ___   ___ ___ ___   ___ ___ ___ ___ ___
A-2 C-4 A-6   B-5 B-3   E-5 C-8 B-8   D-8 B-2 D-2 B-5 A-8

___ ___   ___ ___ ___ .
B-5 E-6   B-1 B-5 A-4

D&C 27:15–18

D&C 14

Use the clues below to complete the crossword puzzle. Read D&C 14 to solve the crossword puzzle.

ACROSS:

5. If we put all our efforts into the Lord's work, we will gain everlasting _____.

6. What did the Lord say was "white already to harvest?"

7. What did David Whitmer later become one of?

8. What is one of the things we must do to have eternal life?

DOWN:

1. What is the greatest of all the gifts of God?

2. Jesus is a "light which cannot be hid in _____."

3. What must we have when we ask the Father in Jesus' name?

4. Whom is this revelation to?

JOSEPH SMITH

When Joseph Smith was the prophet, the Saints completed the first temple in this dispensation. Trace the dots to complete the picture and then read D&C 109 to find out the name of this great building.

TITHING

The missing letters in each alphabet give us a very important message about why we pay our tithing. Discover which letter of the alphabet is missing from each line and write it in the spaces below in order.

1. BCDEFGHIJKLMNOPQRSTUVWXYZ
2. ABCDEFGHIJKMNOPQRSTUVWXYZ
3. ABCDEFGHIJKMNOPQRSTUVWXYZ
4. ABCDEFGHIJKLMNOPQRSUVWXYZ
5. ABCDEFGIJKLMNOPQRSTUVWXYZ
6. ABCDEFGHJKLMNOPQRSTUVWXYZ
7. ABCDEFGHIJKLMOPQRSTUVWXYZ
8. ABCDEFHIJKLMNOPQRSTUVWXYZ
9. ABCDEFGHIJKLMNOPQRTUVWXYZ
10. ACDEFGHIJKLMNOPQRSTUVWXYZ
11. ABCDFGHIJKLMNOPQRSTUVWXYZ
12. ABCDEFGHIJKMNOPQRSTUVWXYZ
13. ABCDEFGHIJKLMNPQRSTUVWXYZ
14. ABCDEFGHIJKLMOPQRSTUVWXYZ
15. ABCDEFHIJKLMNOPQRSTUVWXYZ
16. ABCDEFGHIJKLMNOPQRSUVWXYZ
17. ABCDEFGHIJKLMNPQRSTUVWXYZ
18. ABCDEFGHIJKLMNOPQRSUVWXYZ
19. ABCDEFGIJKLMNOPQRSTUVWXYZ
20. ABCDFGHIJKLMNOPQRSTUVWXYZ
21. ABCDEFGHIJKMNOPQRSTUVWXYZ
22. ABCDEFGHIJKLMNPQRSTUVWXYZ
23. ABCDEFGHIJKLMNOPQSTUVWXYZ
24. ABCEFGHIJKLMNOPQRSTUVWXYZ

___ ___ ___   ___ ___ ___ ___ ___ ___   ___ ___ ___ ___ ___ ___

___ ___   ___ ___ ___   ___ ___ ___ ___ ___ .

FOOD SCRAMBLE

Unscramble the blocks by answering the questions and writing the words listed above into the correct blocks.

broiled fish	loaves and	bread
wild honey	and cumin	mint
figs	comb	five barley
unleavened	and honey	anise
grapes and	locusts and	two fishes

1. Garden herbs and spices that were paid as tithing by the scribes and Pharisees. (Matthew 23:23)

2. The Savior ate this food with his Apostles after being resurrected. (Luke 24:42–43)

3. Jesus talks about these at the end of the Sermon on the Mount. (Matthew 7:16)

4. John the Baptist ate these two things. (Mark 1:6)

5. Jesus blessed this food and then fed 5,000 people. (John 6:9–13)

6. The Savior and his Apostles ate this food as part of the Passover. (Luke 22:1)

NEPHI KNOWLEDGE

Use the clues below to complete the crossword puzzle. See 1 Nephi chapters 1–5 to solve the crossword puzzle if you need help.

ACROSS:

1. Who was the wicked man who had the plates?
4. Nephi's faithful older brother's name.
5. Nephi's father's name.
7. Nephi's mother's name.
8. What did Nephi's family live in in the wilderness?
9. He was one of Laban's servants, who chose to join Nephi and his family in the wilderness.

DOWN:

2. What did Nephi and his brothers return to Jerusalem to get the first time?
3. Where was Nephi's family from?
6. Nephi and his brothers also returned to Jerusalem to get this person's family.

THE SABBATH DAY

What was the fifth commandment given to Moses and the children of Israel? Write the letter that comes after the given letter to see what this commandment was. (For this puzzle, A follows Z.) Then find the words in the word search.

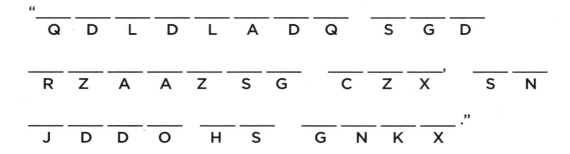

"__ __ __ __ __ __ __ __ __ __ __
 Q D L D L A D Q   S G D

__ __ __ __ __ __ __ __ __ __, __ __
 R Z A A Z S G   C Z X   S N

__ __ __ __ __ __ __ __ __ __."
 J D D O   H S   G N K X

Exodus 20:8

```
R E E K K T O C S N
D E E H Q N N M A Y
X E M R T Y G B B H
P M H E R A M X B C
H U T O M D K P A K
S S K V C B X F T S
X G W X X U E A H G
Y L O H Y T X R I N
Z X V V I Z O B M F
```

A SURPRISE BLESSING

Zacharias was a priest in New Testament times. An angel appeared to him and told him he would have a son. He did not believe the angel and was struck dumb. Soon after, Zacharias had a son just as the angel promised. To find the name of his son, draw a straight line from the first part of each word on the top line to the last part of the word in the second line. Start and end your line on the ▪. Then write the letters crossed by the lines you have made in order in the blanks at the bottom. The first answer is done for you.

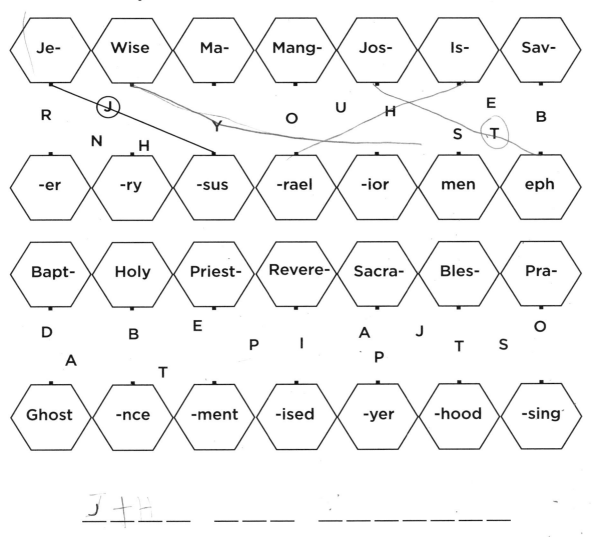

CHARITY

Use the clues below to complete the crossword puzzle. Read 1 Corinthians 13:4–7 if you need help.

ACROSS:
4. "Thinketh no _____."
5. Charity doesn't rejoice in _____.
7. "Is not easily _____."
8. 1st word in verse 7.
10. "Charity _____ long."

DOWN:
1. "Charity is the pure _____ of Christ.
2. "Charity _____ not."
3. The 11th word in verse 4.
6. "Doth not behave itself _____ _____."
9. "Rejoiceth in the _____."

THE LIGHT OF THE SAVIOR

Find the words from John 14:6 that are listed below. Then read the unused letters in the top 3 rows to find a hidden message about the Savior.

```
O  C  W  A  Y  U  O  R  L  I  G  T  J
H  T  O  I  N  F  T  M  T  H  R  E  E
D  A  R  M  A  K  N  I  N  U  E  S  S
S  A  X  T  E  W  U  H  T  M  Y  L  U
O  T  H  K  O  T  U  H  Q  M  B  V  S
W  E  L  D  E  N  H  K  T  A  F  R  J
R  B  N  I  Y  X  Y  U  A  N  D  F  O
R  A  W  F  F  A  B  Z  G  N  F  M  R
H  T  I  A  S  E  O  F  E  H  T  L  O
D  G  D  Y  S  N  Q  U  H  O  P  F  K
K  A  K  H  R  Q  W  G  R  B  P  Q  L
```

AND	BUT	COMETH
FATHER	HIM	JESUS
LIFE	MAN	SAITH
THE	TRUTH	UNTO
WAY		

___ _____ __

___ _____

THE SECOND COMING

What does the Lord want us to do to prepare for his coming? Follow the path that makes a sentence to find out! See 1 Nephi 10:8 if you get stuck.

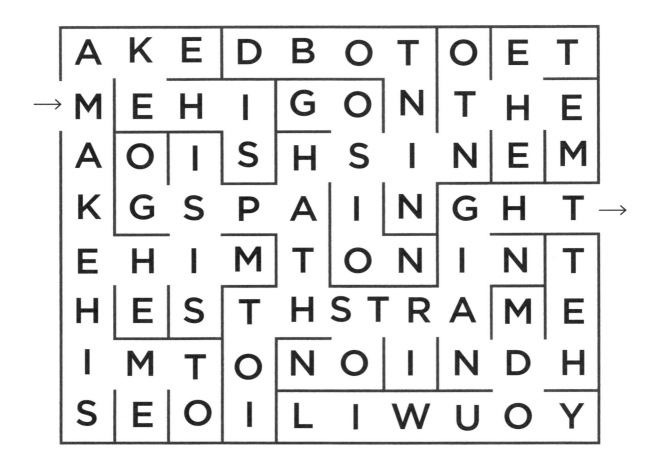

BRIGHAM YOUNG

Complete the dot-to-dot to see the picture of the second prophet of the Church and the temple that he had a vision of.

FAITH FIRST

Cross out every B, X, D, Z, Q, and J to discover the important message that Ether gave us about faith. Write the remaining letters in the spaces below. Look up Ether 12: 6 if you need help.

```
Y  B  E  X  R  D  E  C  Z  E  J  I  D
V  E  Q  N  B  O  X  W  Z  J  I  T  D
N  B  D  E  X  S  S  Q  U  N  Z  J  T
I  L  X  J  Q  A  F  B  D  T  E  X  R
J  T  Z  D  H  B  E  T  Q  R  D  B  I
A  J  L  Z  B  O  X  F  J  B  Y  O  Q
U  R  X  Q  F  D  A  I  B  D  T  X  H
```

"___ ___   ___ ___ ___ ___ ___ ___   ___ ___

___ ___ ___ ___ ___ ___ ___   ___ ___ ___ ___ ___

___ ___ ___ ___ ___   ___ ___ ___   ___ ___ ___ ___ ___

___ ___   ___ ___ ___ ___   ___ ___ ___ ___ ___."

A GREAT PROPHET

Complete the dot-to-dot of Joseph Smith.

A LOT OF FAITH!

The word "faith" is found 16 times in the letter square below. Look backwards, up, down, sideways, and diagonally to find them all.

```
F  A  I  T  F  A  I  H  I
A  F  A  I  T  H  T  H  F
I  I  I  H  T  I  A  F  A
T  T  H  F  A  I  T  H  I
H  F  T  F  A  I  T  H  T
H  A  I  H  F  A  I  T  H
T  I  A  F  A  T  F  I  F
I  T  F  A  I  T  H  A  H
A  H  F  H  T  I  A  F  I
F  A  I  T  H  F  A  I  T
```

PRIESTHOOD POWER!

Read the following scripture about the priesthood. Unscramble the key words taken from the scripture and place the numbered letters in the blanks with the same number at the bottom of the page to find our which prophets received this power from the Lord and the scripture reference.

"I give unto power, that whatsoever ye shall seal on earth shall be sealed in heaven; and whatsoever ye shall loose on earth shall be loosed in heaven."

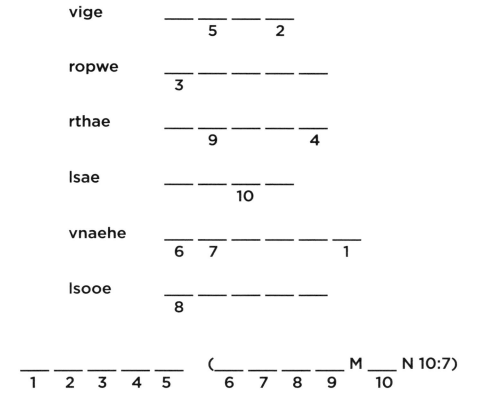

vige   ___ ___ ___ ___
                 5   2

ropwe   ___ ___ ___ ___ ___
           3

rthae   ___ ___ ___ ___ ___
               9   4

lsae   ___ ___ ___ ___
                 10

vnaehe   ___ ___ ___ ___ ___ ___
             6   7   1

lsooe   ___ ___ ___ ___ ___
           8

___ ___ ___ ___ ___   (___ ___ ___ ___ M ___ N 10:7)
 1   2   3   4   5   6   7   8   9   10

3 NEPHI 13:6–20

Complete the crossword puzzle. Use 3 Nephi 13:6–20 if you need help.

ACROSS:

2. Heavenly Father will forgive us our _____ if we will forgive others.

4. We should ask Heavenly Father to help us overcome _____.

7. When we pray, we are told not to use vain _____.

8. When we fast in secret, Heavenly Father will reward us _____.

DOWN:

1. We should forgive our _____ _____ as Heavenly Father forgives our debts.

3. The last word in verse 10.

5. "Lay not up for yourselves _____ upon earth."

6. Heavenly Father already knows what we _____ before we ask him.

TEMPLE FACTS

Discover which letter of the alphabet is missing from each line and write it in order in the spaces below to finish the sentence.

The Kirtland Ohio Temple was the first temple . . .

1. ACDEFGHIJKLMNOPQRSTUVWXYZ
2. ABCDEFGHIJKLMNOPQRSTVWXYZ
3. ABCDEFGHJKLMNOPQRSTUVWXYZ
4. ABCDEFGHIJKMNOPQRSTUVWXYZ
5. ABCDEFGHIJKLMNOPQRSUVWXYZ
6. ABCDEFGHJKLMNOPQRSTUVWXYZ
7. ABCDEFGHIJKLMOPQRSTUVWXYZ
8. ABCDEFGHIJKLMNOPQRSUVWXYZ
9. ABCDEFGIJKLMNOPQRSTUVWXYZ
10. ABCDEFGHJKLMNOPQRSTUVWXYZ
11. ABCDEFGHIJKLMNOPQRTUVWXYZ
12. ABCEFGHIJKLMNOPQRSTUVWXYZ
13. ABCDEFGHJKLMNOPQRSTUVWXYZ
14. ABCDEFGHIJKLMNOPQRTUVWXYZ
15. ABCDEFGHIJKLMNOQRSTUVWXYZ
16. ABCDFGHIJKLMNOPQRSTUVWXYZ
17. ABCDEFGHIJKLMOPQRSTUVWXYZ
18. ABCDEFGHIJKLMNOPQRTUVWXYZ
19 BCDEFGHIJKLMNOPQRSTUVWXYZ
20. ABCDEFGHIJKLMNOPQRSUVWXYZ
21. ABCDEFGHJKLMNOPQRSTUVWXYZ
22. ABCDEFGHIJKLMNPQRSTUVWXYZ
23. ABCDEFGHIJKLMOPQRSTUVWXYZ

. . . __ __ __ __ __   __ __   __ __ __

__ __ __ __ __ __ __ __ __ __ __ __.

WHICH ARTICLE OF FAITH?

Find the words listed below in the word search. Then write the unused letters in the spaces, starting in the top row, to find out which Article of Faith these words are from.

```
T  H  E  D  E  L  A  E  V  E  R  N  I
T  N  A  T  R  O  P  M  I  N  G  T  H
W  A  R  T  I  S  E  C  L  E  R  O  F
F  O  A  I  E  T  K  V  H  P  E  G  T
U  D  N  O  E  O  A  I  E  A  A  E  U
U  P  D  B  S  P  M  R  N  I  T  F  H
P  E  R  T  A  I  N  I  N  G  L  F  K
U  N  T  X  N  D  F  H  N  Y  D  E  E
Z  E  D  J  E  I  O  M  N  S  Z  O  B
Y  S  M  Y  A  R  T  G  D  X  A  Z  M
```

BELIEVE   DOES   GOD
GREAT   IMPORTANT   KINGDOM
NOW   PERTAINING   YET
REVEALED

—— — ——— ——— ——————— ——————

—— ——————

MARY AND JESUS

Complete the dot-to-dot to see the finished picture.

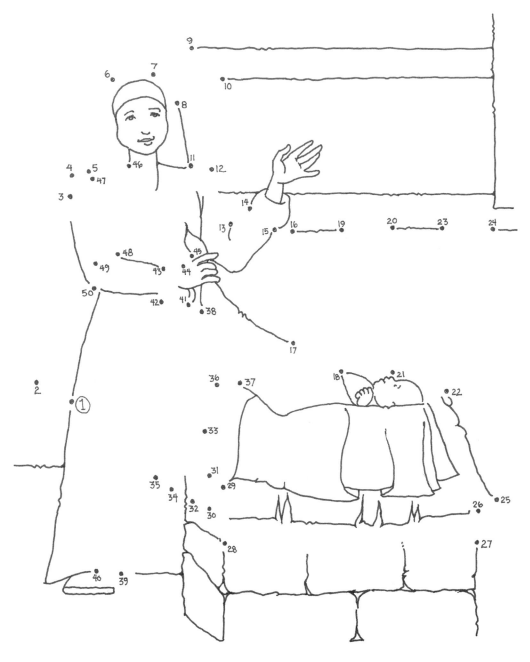

OH ZION!

One word is missing from each of the sentences below. Color the spaces that have any of the letters Z, I, O, or N to find the missing words. Then read 2 Nephi 8:3.

1. In the last days the Lord shall comfort Zion and will comfort all her _____ places.

Z	T	R	C	Z	J	I	Z	O	L	N	I	Z	G	N	O	I	F	N	I	Z
N	X	L	E	O	F	O	J	N	D	O	H	B	C	E	Z	C	B	O	H	B
O	Y	I	D	N	H	O	N	I	G	Z	O	N	J	D	I	G	E	Z	N	D
I	Z	A	O	I	F	I	D	Z	C	K	D	I	B	E	O	B	G	Z	K	C
Z	B	E	G	O	P	Z	M	O	C	Z	N	O	C	L	N	P	M	I	O	N

2. The Lord will make her wilderness like _____.

N	Z	I	D	Z	I	L	A	I	Z	N	H	Z	C	A	I
I	A	C	B	I	H	O	R	N	D	B	E	I	I	D	Z
O	N	F	M	N	E	N	J	Z	O	A	G	N	A	O	O
Z	F	A	C	Z	K	I	P	O	Q	F	E	I	B	A	Z
I	O	N	B	O	Z	F	C	N	I	Z	A	O	D	E	I

3. And he will make Zion's desert like the garden of the _____.

Z	R	E	A	Z	O	I	A	Z	I	O	B	O	Z	S
O	E	S	B	I	R	O	S	I	C	Z	A	Z	E	N
I	C	T	E	O	X	N	Y	O	N	P	X	N	C	I
N	A	C	X	N	Y	O	P	I	M	Z	M	Z	A	Z
Z	I	O	R	I	Z	I	M	N	A	I	P	I	O	S

4. _____ and gladness shall be found therein.

R	I	N	Z	X	N	Z	I	M	Z	X	Z
B	X	Z	Y	S	I	P	N	B	I	R	I
C	A	I	E	D	Z	Q	O	D	O	N	O
I	P	O	U	A	N	E	Z	F	R	I	P
Z	O	N	B	T	O	I	N	L	T	O	S

5. Thanksgiving and the voice of _____.

Z	A	S	R	I	G	I	Z	O	H	N	H	L	T	Z	I	O	H	I	O	U	C	Z	H	I
I	O	C	N	Z	R	N	X	B	C	O	F	G	D	O	S	N	R	N	K	N	X	N	P	O
O	K	N	E	Z	U	O	N	F	S	Z	G	S	C	N	L	Z	R	O	C	I	R	O	N	Z
N	M	Y	H	O	X	N	R	A	L	I	T	H	U	O	B	O	F	Z	E	O	A	S	Z	X
Z	X	S	B	N	E	I	Z	O	R	Z	O	N	U	Z	N	N	S	N	Z	B	Y	G	I	T

LET YOUR LIGHT SO SHINE

Read Mosiah 16:9. Draw the other half of the candle.

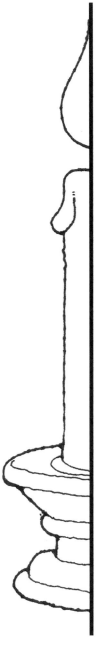

SERVICE

Read Mosiah 2:17. On the first line, write IN ORDER all the lowercase letters and then write IN ORDER all the uppercase letters. Repeat the process on the second line to find out the important truth King Benjamin tells us.

wOhUReFnELLweOsWeMErNIvTe

_____

iSEsRVthINeGsaTmHEeLOaRsD

_____

A BEAUTIFUL PROMISE

As a sign of his promise to the prophet Noah that he would never again destroy the earth by flooding, the Lord put something in the sky. Read Genesis 6:13–22 and unscramble the words below that are found in those verses. Copy the letters in the numbered cells to the spaces with the same number to find out what the Lord put in the sky.

COILVEEN   __ (3) __ __ __ __ __ __

HOAN   (4) __ __ __

SYODETR   __ __ __ __ (1) __ __

RAK   (2) __ __

LDFOO   __ __ (5) __ __

CEVTOANN   __ __ __ __ __ __

OFWSL   __ __ (6) __ __

MEDDOCNAM   __ __ __ __ __ __ __ __ __

__ __ __ __ B __ __
1   2   3   4   5   6

NEW TESTAMENT LETTER SQUARE

Find each book of the New Testament by reading forward, backward, up, down, and diagonally. The number of times to find each word is indicated in parenthesis.

Matthew (2)　　Romans (2)　　Colossians (2)　　Hebrews (2)
Mark (4)　　Corinthians (2)　　Thessalonians (1)　　James (1)
Luke (3)　　Galatians (3)　　Timothy (2)　　Peter (2)
Ephesians (2)　　Titus (2)　　John (4)　　Revelation (1)
Acts (3)　　Philippians (1)　　Philemon (1)　　Jude (3)

B	P	R	M	I	C	O	L	O	S	S	I	A	N	S	U	T	I	I	J
K	H	R	O	M	A	N	S	R	T	S	U	J	O	C	J	A	O	N	A
J	I	M	R	A	C	T	S	C	T	X	Y	O	J	O	H	N	L	M	M
D	L	R	E	T	V	C	A	J	U	D	E	H	H	R	D	A	J	A	E
E	I	L	V	T	L	Y	U	R	O	M	A	N	S	I	R	P	G	T	S
L	P	P	W	H	X	M	O	J	O	H	N	S	N	N	E	U	A	T	P
N	P	Q	U	E	P	H	E	S	I	A	N	S	X	T	T	R	L	H	N
H	I	R	S	W	E	R	B	E	H	B	A	E	E	H	E	M	A	E	X
O	A	C	T	S	L	U	I	M	A	R	K	R	Y	I	P	A	T	W	E
J	N	S	U	J	U	D	E	H	R	U	I	H	X	A	Z	R	I	T	C
P	S	T	H	P	K	S	G	A	L	A	T	I	A	N	S	K	A	N	E
R	I	L	U	R	E	D	U	J	A	S	W	L	H	S	R	F	N	L	O
T	S	N	A	I	T	A	L	A	G	F	M	O	L	A	F	G	S	E	D
T	I	M	O	T	H	Y	P	H	J	K	J	L	M	X	R	S	K	T	S
G	T	H	E	S	S	A	L	O	N	I	A	N	S	E	N	U	M	R	P
C	C	O	R	I	N	T	H	I	A	N	S	B	J	D	L	T	K	E	C
G	H	R	J	R	E	V	E	L	A	T	I	O	N	Y	O	F	U	T	E
V	F	H	I	I	E	P	H	E	S	I	A	N	S	J	P	T	H	E	N
C	O	L	O	S	S	I	A	N	S	T	I	I	G	Q	Z	I	H	P	R
W	H	S	W	E	R	B	E	H	L	U	K	E	U	S	G	B	C	P	I
T	I	M	O	T	H	Y	W	G	C	S	P	H	I	L	E	M	O	N	S

HEAVENLY VISITOR

Before Joseph was given the golden plates, he was visited by a heavenly being three times. To find what who Joseph's visitor was, write the name of each picture in the corresponding lines. The shaded boxes will give you the answer.

1.

2.

3.

4.

5.

SCRAMBLED SCRIPTURE

Using the directions below, change each letter in the puzzle to reveal the scripture. Look up James 2:17 if you need help.

Change all H's to E's.
Change all F's to H's.
Change all I's to V's.
Change all E's to N's.
Change all L's to S's.
Change all A's to O's.
Change all U's to F's.
Change all X's to I's
Change all B's to A's.

Change all Z'x to G's.
Change all C's to W's.
Change all Q's to R's.
Change all N's to K's.
Change all G's to D's.
Change all P's to L's.
Change all W's to B's.
Change all O's to T's.

"E V E N   S O   F A I T H ,   I F
 H I H E   L A   U B X O F   X U

I T   H A T H   N O T   W O R K S ,
X O   F B O F   E A O   C A Q N L

I S   D E A D ,   B E I N G
X L   G H B G   W H X E Z

A L O N E ."
B P A E H

CHANGE OF HEART

Alma the Younger and the sons of Mosiah were rebellious men. They sought to destroy the Church. An angel appeared to them and commanded them to stop. Follow the directions below, then read the remaining words on the table from left to right to find out what happened after the angel appeared to them. (See Mosiah 27:8–17, 32, 36.)

1. Cross out all words with 13 or more letters.
2. Cross out all the names of fruits.
3. Cross out all the names of states.
4. Cross out all the names of sounds.
5. Cross out all words starting with "y."
6. Cross out all the names of drinks.
7. Cross out all the names of animals.

neighborhoods	apple	yesterday	juice
Alma	milk	and	buzz
Hawaii	the	sons	water
bang	strawberry	soda pop	of
Nebuchadnezzar	Alaska	dog	Georgia
Mosiah	yes	raspberry	yogurt
cows	hum	repented	banana
cat	and	snake	became
oranges	yule	squeal	horse
great	rabbit	duck	missionaries.

SCRAMBLED SCRIPTURE

Decode the scripture by first filling in all of the words that you recognize. Then take the numbered letters and fill them in throughout the rest of the puzzle. Read Ephesians 4:32 if you get stuck.

A	B	C	D	E	F	G	H	I	J	K	L	M	N	O	P	Q	R	S	T
15			21		7	22	17							5					8

U	V	W	X	Y	Z

"A__ D__ __ __ __ __ __ __ __ __ D__ O__ __ __
 15 1 21 18 20 23 20 9 19 1 21 5 1 20

T__ O__ __ A__ __ O__ T__ H__ __ __,
8 5   15 1 5 8 17 20 12

T__ __ __ D__ __ __ H__ __ A__ __ T__ __ D__,
8 20 1 21 20 12 17 20 15 12 8 20 21

F__ O__ __ G__ __ __ __ __ __ G__ O__ __ __
7 5 12 22 19 10 19 1 22 5 1 20

A__ __ O__ T__ H__ __ __ __ __ __ __ __ A__ __
15 1 5 8 17 20 12 20 10 20 1 15 14

G__ O__ D__ F__ O__ __ __ H__ __ __ __ __ T', __ A__ __ __
22 5 20 15 1 12 25 17 12 19 14 8 14 14 15 9 20

H__ A__ T__ H__ F__ O__ __ G__ __ __ __ __ __ __ O__ __."
17 15 8 17 7 5 12 22 19 10 20 1 23 5 26

AN ACT OF LOVE

What does service mean to you? Read Mosiah 2:17 and solve the puzzle below.

A	B	C	D	E	F	G	H	I	J	K	L	M	N	O	P	Q	R	S	T
				20	7								24		19			6	16

U	V	W	X	Y	Z
8					

S E _ _ _ _ E   _ S   _ N
6 20 11 22 10 23 20   10 6   3 24

_ _ T   T _ _ T   U P _ _ _ T S,
3 23 16 16 25 3 16 8 19 12 10 7 16 6

E N _ _ U _ _ _ E S,   _ _
20 24 23 21 8 11 3 17 20 6   21 11

_ E _ P S   _ N _ T _ E _
25 20 12 19 6   3 24 21 16 25 20 11

P E _ S _ N.
19 20 11 6 21 24

FOLLOW THE PROPHET

Find the words "Follow the Prophet" by starting at the arrow and following the correct letters by moving right, left, up, down, or diagonally and using no letter more than once. After you find all the words, write the unused letters (reading left to right, top to bottom) on the blanks below to find out why it is important to follow the prophet.

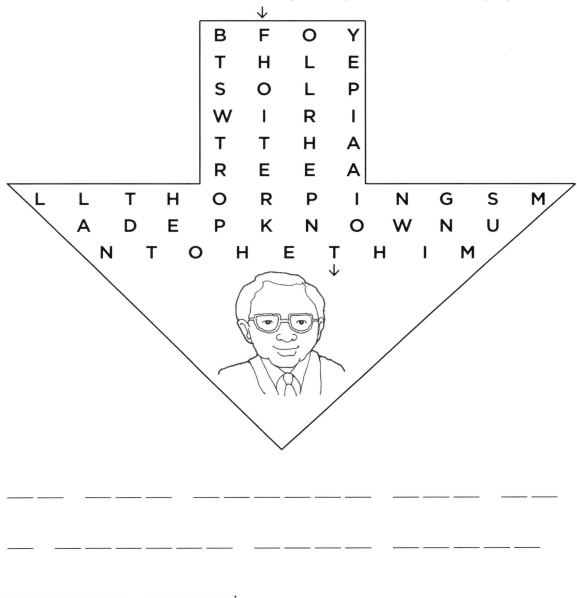

↓

```
        B   F   O   Y
        T   H   L   E
        S   O   L   P
        W   I   R   I
        T   T   H   A
        R   E   E   A
L   L   T   H   O   R   P   I   N   G   S   M
A   D   E   P   K   N   O   W   N   U
    N   T   O   H   E   T   H   I   M
                        ↓
```

___ ___   ___ ___ ___   ___ ___ ___ ___ ___ ___ ___   ___ ___ ___   ___ ___

___   ___ ___ ___ ___ ___ ___   ___ ___ ___   ___ ___ ___ ___ ___

___ ___ ___ ___ ___   ___ ___ ___ ___.

A GREAT BLESSING

The Lord told Abraham that he would bless his wife, Sariah. Figure out which letter belongs with each clue. Then fill in the same letter in all the boxes with the same number. Read the boxes left to right to find out what the Lord blessed Sariah to be.

1. If you swap the "s" in "sun" for this letter, you would be having a good time.
2. This letter plus "nt" makes a small insect.
3. This letter is in "steer" but not in "peers."
4. This letter is a consonant in "middle," but not in "fiddle."
5. If you look in "meow," this letter will be there once. But in "pool" and "school," it will be twice.
6. If you add this letter to "pat," you'll have something you can follow that will lead you somewhere.
7. You'll find me in "now" and "then," but not in "future."

2.	4.	5.	3.
6.	E	R	5.
1.	7.	2.	3.
I	5.	7.	S

— — — — — —   — —   — — — — — —

SCRAMBLED SCRIPTURE

Read the following scripture and unscramble some of the key words from it. Place the numbered letters in the correct blanks at the bottom to reveal the scripture reference. Then find the unscrambled words in the mini word search.

"I, the Lord, am bound when ye do what I say; but when ye do not what I say, ye have no promise."

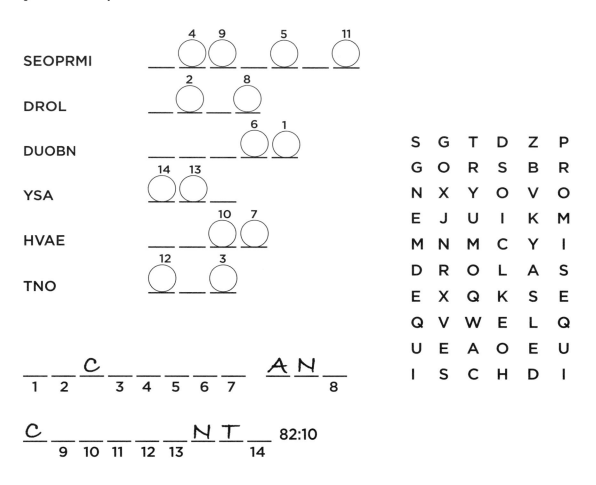

SEOPRMI ___ ⓸ ⓽ ___ ⓹ ___ ⓫

DROL ___ ② ⑧

DUOBN ___ ___ ___ ⑥ ①

YSA ⑭ ⑬ ___

HVAE ___ ___ ⑩ ⑦

TNO ⑫ ___ ③

___ ___ C ___ ___ ___ ___ ___   A N ___
 1   2   3   4   5   6   7   8

C ___ ___ ___ ___ ___ N T ___   82:10
   9 10 11 12 13   14

S	G	T	D	Z	P
G	O	R	S	B	R
N	X	Y	O	V	O
E	J	U	I	K	M
M	N	M	C	Y	I
D	R	O	L	A	S
E	X	Q	K	S	E
Q	V	W	E	L	Q
U	E	A	O	E	U
I	S	C	H	D	I

SHARING THE GOSPEL

Decode the puzzle to find a few of the ways you can share the gospel.

A	B	C	D	E	F	G	H	I	J	K	L	M	N	O	P	Q	R	S	T
17	4			19						12								15	

U	V	W	X	Y	Z
			20	25	

B Y   S E _ _ _ _ _   A _ _ _ _
4 25   15 19 14 14 23 21 26   17 26 13 13 22

E X A _ _ _ E,   _ _ _ _ _ _ _ _ _ _
19 20 17 3 24 16 19   23 21 9 23 14 23 14 23 21 26

_ E _ _ _ B _ S _ _
21 19 23 26 6 4 13 2 15 14 13

_ _ _ _ _ _ A _ _ _ _ _ _ E S,
18 6 10 2 18 6 17 18 14 23 9 23 14 23 19 15

_ _ _ E _ S _ _ _ _ _ _ A _ _
7 2 23 19 21 22 15 6 23 24 24 23 21 26 17 21 22

A S K _ _ _ _ _ _ _ E Y
17 18 12 23 21 26 23 7 14 6 19 25

_ _ _ _ _ _ _ K E _ _ _ K _ _ _
5 13 10 16 22 16 23 12 19 14 13 12 21 13 5

A B _ _ _ _ _ E _ _ _ _ _ _.
17 4 13 10 14 14 6 19 18 6 10 2 18 6

1 SAMUEL 17:32–51

After you read 1 Samuel 17:32–51, figure out the clues to solve the crossword puzzle.

ACROSS

3. What did David use as his weapon?

6. David worked in his father's field as a _____.

7. How many stones did David have?

DOWN

1. Where did the stone hit Goliath?

2. Goliath the giant was a _____.

3. Goliath had a _____, shield, and spear.

4. "This day will the Lord _____ thee into my hand."

5. David had protected his father's sheep from a lion and a _____.

WHO IS THIS MAN?

Trace the dots to find out. If you need help, read Mosiah 11:20.

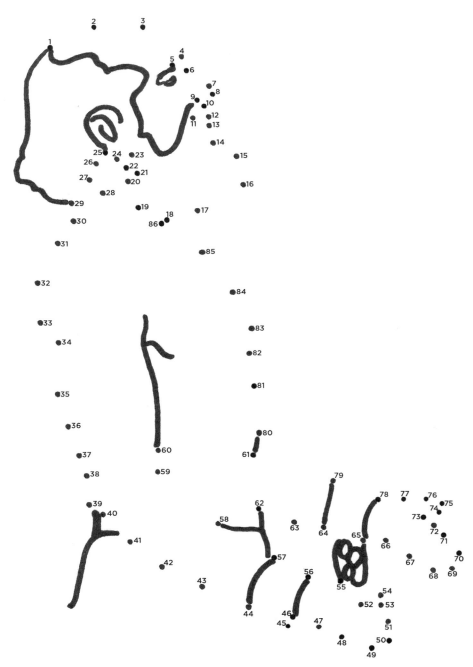

MOSIAH 7:1–17

King Limhi gives his people an important message. Read Mosiah 7:1–17. Number each event in the order it occurred. Next, place the letter for that number in the correct spaces below to find out what this message was.

O _____   They wander 40 days in the wilderness.

D _____   King Limhi asks them why they were near the walls of his city.

N _____   They are taken to see the king and commanded to answer his questions.

R _____   Ammon is made leader over the group.

I _____   Limhi sends a proclamation to his people to gather themselves together at the temple.

E _____   Limhi was glad to know his brethren in Zarahemla were alive.

U _____   Mosiah wants to know how the people in Lehi-Nephi were doing.

H _____   Ammon and his men are in prison for 2 days.

S _____   King Limhi tells Ammon to eat, drink, and rest.

T _____   Mosiah appoints 16 men to travel to Lehi-Nephi.

W _____   Ammon tells the king his name and that they came up to inquire about them.

F _____   Limhi tells Ammon that they are in bondage to the Lamanites.

L _____   Limhi told Ammon that it would be better to be slaves to the Nephites than to pay taxes to the king of the Lamanites.

P _____   Ammon takes 3 of his men down into the land of Nephi and they are taken by the king's guard.

Limhi tells his people that if they would "___ ___ ___ ___   ___ ___
          2   1   3   7   2   4

___ ___ ___   ___ ___ ___ ___   ___ ___ ___ ___   ___ ___ ___ ___
2   6   10   12   4   3   8   9   14   2   6   11   1   12   12

___ ___ ___ ___ ___ ___ ___   ___ ___   ___ ___ᵃ   ___ ___ . . ."
5   1   3   5   4   13   10   4   11   6   10   3   2

the Lord would deliver them out of bondage.

ARTICLES OF FAITH

Decode this Article of Faith. Assign numbers to the boxed letters at the top as they correspond the Article of Faith below. Then fill in the rest of the letters.

A	B	C	D	E	F	G	H	I	J	K	L	M	N	O	P	Q	R	S	T
							8										6	1	

U	V	W	X	Y	Z
		16			

"W __   __ __ L I __ __ __   __ __ __
16 2   10 2 3 8 2 14 2   22 24 2

__ I __ L __   __ __   __ __   __ __ __
10 8 10 3 2   22 25   10 2   22 24 2

W __ R __   __ __   __ __ __   __ S   __ __ R
16 23 6 13   23 21   7 23 13   11 1   21 11 6

__ S __ I __   I S   __ R __ __ S L __ __ __
11 1 8 22   8 1   22 6 11 5 1 3 11 22 2 13

__ __ R __ __ __ __ L __;   W __   __ L S __
4 23 6 2 2 4 22 3 12   16 2   11 3 1 23

__ __ L I __ __ __   __ __ __   __ __ __ __
10 2 3 8 2 14 2   22 24 2   10 23 23 26

__ __   __ __ R __ __   __ __   __ __   __ __ __
23 21   20 23 6 20 23 3   22 23   10 2   22 24 2

__ W __ R __   __ __ __   __ __ __ __."
16 23 6 13   23 21   7 23 13

THE SACRAMENT

Solve the math problems in each of the boxes. Circle the words in each box where the solution to the problem is 12. Then write each word in order in the spaces at the bottom to find out why we take the sacrament.

5+4+6=_____ THIS	6+7-1=_____ IN	10+4-1=_____ YE	15+2-5=_____ REMEMBRANCE
7+7-2=_____ OF	5+5-1=_____ DO	10+1+1=_____ THE	4+8-3=_____ NIGHT
6+6+2=_____ DRINK	10-1+4=_____ THANKS	14+2-6=_____ ME	20-9+1=_____ SACRIFICE
7+3+2=_____ JESUS	18-2+6=_____ EAT	4+7+3=_____ CUP	14+4-6+_____ MADE

_____

_____

THE SAD RICH MAN

A rich young man asked Jesus what he needed to do to gain eternal life. Jesus told him to sell everything he had and follow him. To find out what the rich young man did, first work each math problem. Then, beginning with the answer that equals 1, write the words in the lines below.

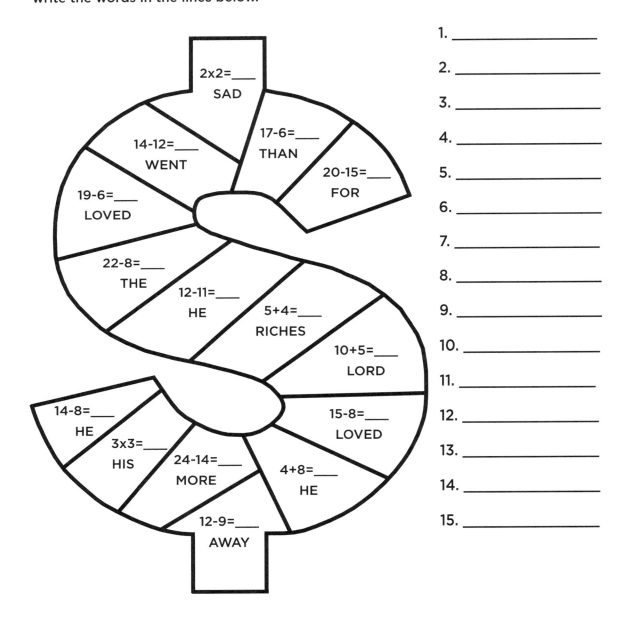

2x2=____ SAD

17-6=____ THAN

14-12=____ WENT

20-15=____ FOR

19-6=____ LOVED

22-8=____ THE

12-11=____ HE

5+4=____ RICHES

10+5=____ LORD

14-8=____ HE

15-8=____ LOVED

3x3=____ HIS

24-14=____ MORE

4+8=____ HE

12-9=____ AWAY

1. _____

2. _____

3. _____

4. _____

5. _____

6. _____

7. _____

8. _____

9. _____

10. _____

11. _____

12. _____

13. _____

14. _____

15. _____

THE FISHERMEN

Read the scripture below about what Jesus said to Simon Peter and his brother Andrew as they were fishing in the sea of Galilee. Then to find out what happened next, write the numbered letters on the blanks with the same numbers.

"AND HE SAITH UNTO THEM, FOLLOW ME,
14   7   2   6   5   12   4   1

AND I WILL MAKE YOU FISHERS OF MEN."
10   9   15   8   3   11   13

"A N D t h e y S t R A I G h t w A y
14 2 10 6 3 1 8 7 6 11 14 9 3 6 4 14 8

L e F t t h e I R N e t S A N d
12 1 5 6 6 3 1 9 11 2 1 6 7 14 2 10

F o l l o w e d H I M."
5 13 12 12 13 4 1 10 3 9 15

Matthew 4:19

THE GOLDEN PLATES

Using the picture of the plates on this page, redraw the plates in the graph on the next page.

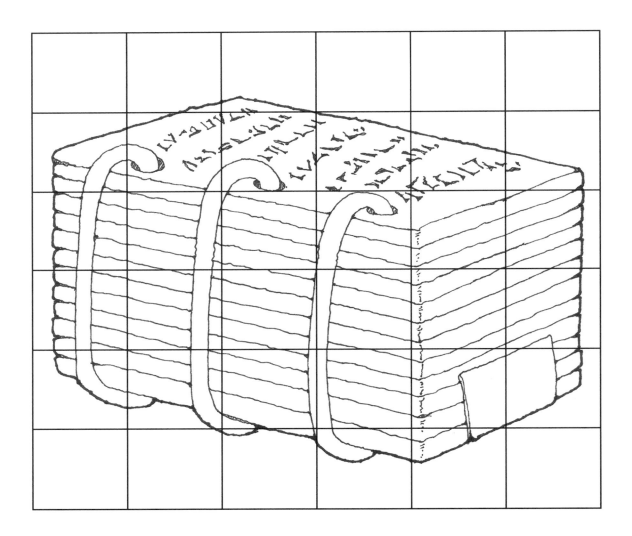

HAROLD B. LEE

Read this prophet's biographical sketch and find the underlined words in the word search.

Harold B. Lee was born on March 28, 1899, in Clifton, <u>Idaho</u>. President Lee developed careers in <u>education</u>, business, and <u>government</u>. He was <u>president</u> of the Salt Lake <u>Pioneer</u> Stake during the Great Depression and initiated a program that later became the <u>Welfare</u> System of the Church. In 1941, he was called to the Quorum of the Twelve Apostles. The organization changes he initiated helped the Church during its rapid <u>expansion</u>. On July 7, 1972, Harold B. Lee was called to be the president of the Church. He traveled often and frequently addressing the <u>youth</u> of the Church. He died on December 26, 1973 after serving 18 <u>months</u> as Church President.

```
Z  E  P  U  O  T  N  E  D  I  S  E  R  P  Z
V  I  D  A  H  O  O  X  I  B  Y  R  K  D  N
R  Y  A  U  D  M  S  P  J  B  M  A  M  M  O
P  E  O  G  C  H  X  A  N  P  G  F  M  G  A
B  X  E  U  T  A  Z  N  H  F  Q  L  E  Q  Q
M  P  R  N  T  V  T  S  D  F  I  E  S  D  O
R  P  O  V  O  H  L  I  H  J  B  W  O  T  V
O  M  T  J  O  I  X  O  O  H  G  U  T  I  O
Q  C  Y  A  N  Z  P  N  B  N  R  W  J  V  W
C  H  G  O  V  E  R  N  M  E  N  T  E  P  W
```

WHO IS TO RECEIVE THE GOSPEL

Unscramble each of the clue words. Copy the letters in the numbered circles to the space with the corresponding number below. If you need help, look up scriptures Matthew 24:14, Mark 16:15, Revelations 14:6, and D&C 90:11.

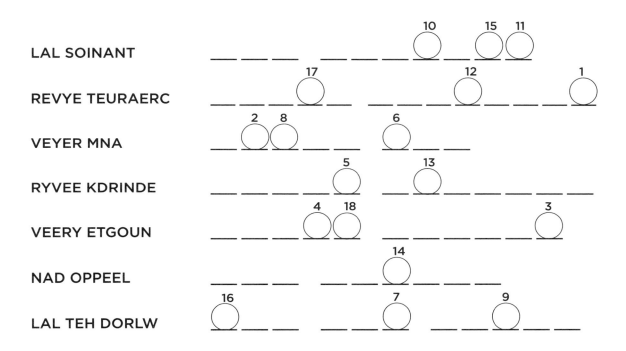

LAL SOINANT

REVYE TEURAERC

VEYER MNA

RYVEE KDRINDE

VEERY ETGOUN

NAD OPPEEL

LAL TEH DORLW

And how are we supposed to help?

___ ___ ___ ___ ___   ___ ___ ___ ___   ___ ___   ___
 1   2   3   4   5   6   7   6   8   9   10 11   12
                                  B

___ ___ ___ ___ ___ ___ ___ ___ ___
 6 13 11 11 13 14 15 16 17 18

A RIGHTEOUS LEADER

Trace the dots to discover who this is. The helmet is numbered separately. If you need help, see Alma 53:22.

FAITH IN GREAT NUMBERS

There were many people in the Bible that showed great faith. To learn about some of them, read the clues and look up the scripture to unscramble their names. Then write the numbered letters in order in the spaces at the bottom to learn the name of the man who was called "the man of faith."

1. She kept faith in God's promise. (Hebrews 11:11)

ARSA ___ ◯(1) ___ ___

2. These people were chosen by God because they were rich in faith. (James 2:5)

ROPO ___ ___ ___ ◯(3)

3. She demonstrated great faith by her actions. (Luke 2:36–37)

NNAA ◯(6) ___ ___ ___

4. This man by his faith was able to do great wonders and miracles. (Acts 6:8)

NEPHETS ___ ___ ___ ___ ◯(5) ___ ___

5. He was martyred for his faith. (Revelation 2:13)

ATINPSA ◯(4) ___ ___ ___ ___ ___ ___

6. One of the three men who were thrown into the fiery furnace but was saved by his faith. (Daniel 3:27–28)

ADEB-GEON ___ ◯(2) ___ ___-
___ ___ ___ ___

7. The Lord prayed that this man would keep his faith. (Luke 22:31-32)

MINSO ___ ___ ◯(7) ___ ___

___ ___ ___ ___ ___ ___ ___
1 2 3 4 5 6 7

A BIRD OF PEACE

When Jesus was baptized, the Holy Ghost descended from Heaven in the form of a dove. Trace the dots to discover the hidden picture.

HEAVENLY LOVE

Heavenly Father sent Jesus to make it possible for us to return to live with him. This shows us that each one of us is important to him. Decode the scripture below by solving each math problem. When you have solved them, find the solution under the lines at the bottom of the page and put the correct letter in each place.

A	13+9=	M	6+13-1=
B	2x6=	N	6x5=
D	6+2-4=	O	3x3=
E	4+4+5=	R	20+11=
F	10-5=	S	4x5=
G	11+7-4=	T	22-7=
H	3x2=	U	3x0=
I	20-6-7=	W	12x2=
L	11x4=		

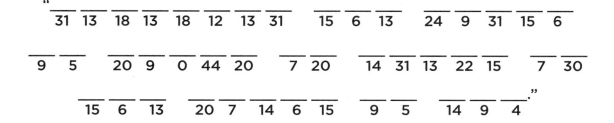

"__ __ __ __ __ __ __ __   __ __ __   __ __ __ __ __
 31 13 18 13 18 12 13 31   15 6 13   24 9 31 15 6

__ __   __ __ __ __ __   __ __   __ __ __ __ __   __ __
 9 5   20 9 0 44 20   7 20   14 31 13 22 15   7 30

__ __ __   __ __ __ __ __   __ __   __ __ __."
15 6 13   20 7 14 6 15   9 5   14 9 4

D&C 18:10

MIGHTY MIRACLES

Read the scripture below and use the numbered letters to fill in the puzzle.
The finished puzzle will tell you what happened next in the story.

"A MAN NAMED JARIUS . . . FELL DOWN AT JESUS' FEET, AND
        10   13   1 5   12

BESOUGHT HIM THAT HE WOULD COME INTO HIS HOUSE: FOR
      8   11 9   3

HE HAD ONE ONLY DAUGHTER, . . . AND SHE LAY DYING."
   7   15   2   6 14   4

___ ___ ___ ___ ___ ___ , ___ ___ ___ ___ ___ ___ ___ ___
 5 7 9 2 3 14   6 7 3 4 8 1 12 2

___ ___ ___   ___ ___ ___ ___   ___ ___ ___   ___ ___ ___ ___ ___
 8 7 6   6 9 12 6   7 10 6   5 12 14 3 14

___ ___ ___ ___ ___ ___   ___ ___ ___   ___ ___ ___ ___
 2 7 9 14 12 6   8 12 2   13 2 15 11

___ ___ ___   ___ ___ ___ ___ .
 1 8 12   6 12 7 6

LUKE 8:41–42, 49–55

PICTURE SEARCH

There are many items hidden in the picture of Mormon burying the golden plates. See if you can find a sock, a hanger, a bow tie, a football, a pair of scissors, a baseball bat, a toothbrush, and a broom.

NEPHI'S SHIP

Use the clues below to complete the crossword puzzle. Read 1 Nephi 17:8–18 to solve the crossword puzzle.

ACROSS:

1. Nephi made _____ to blow on the fire.
3. The Lord commanded Nephi to build a _____.
6. Nephi made tools out of _____.
7. "I did exhort my bretheren to _____"
8. Nephi's brother's called him a _____.

9. Nephi tried to keep the _____.

DOWN:

2. What did Nephi use to make fire?
4. The ship was taking them to the _____ _____.
5. Nephi's brother's did this against him.

A RIGHTEOUS MAN

Unscramble the key words from the story. Each sentence in which the scrambled words can be found is underlined. Then copy the letters in the numbered circles to the spaces with the same number to find out the name of the Lamanite prophet.

The Lamanites had become more righteous than the Nephites. A Lamanite prophet went to Zarahemla to preach to the wicked Nephites. He told them they must repent. But they wouldn't listen and threw him out of their city. On his way back to his own land, the Lord told this prophet to return to Zarahemla. He was to tell the Nephites things what the Lord put into his heart. But the Nephites wouldn't let him back in. So this prophet climbed up on the city's wall and spoke loudly to the people. He prophesied many things to them about the destruction that would come if they did not repent. He also told them that the birth of Jesus Christ would take place in five years and told them of the signs of his birth. He also told them of the signs of Christ's death. Some of the Nephites believed him and repented and were baptized.

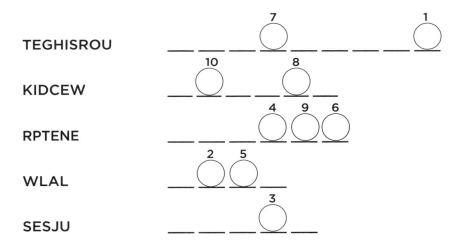

TEGHISROU ___ ___ ___ (7) ___ ___ ___ ___ (1)

KIDCEW ___ (10) ___ ___ (8) ___

RPTENE ___ ___ ___ (4) (9) (6)

WLAL ___ (2) (5) ___

SESJU ___ ___ ___ (3) ___

___ ___ M ___ ___ ___   ___ ___ ___   ___ ___ M ___ ___ ___ ___
 1 2   3 4 5   6 7 8   5 2   2 9 10 6 8

FRUITS OF THE SPIRIT

Fruits of the Spirit are qualities and attitudes that the Heavenly Father and Jesus Christ possess. To become more like them, we must try to develop these in ourselves. Unscramble the words below to find out what some of the fruits of the Spirit are. Then find them in the word search. See Alma 13:28–29 for help.

lveo ___ ___ ___ ___

yjo ___ ___ ___

negltneses ___ ___ ___ ___ ___ ___ ___ ___ ___ ___

inkssdne ___ ___ ___ ___ ___ ___ ___ ___

meksnese ___ ___ ___ ___ ___ ___ ___ ___

ptaceeni ___ ___ ___ ___ ___ ___ ___ ___

ceape ___ ___ ___ ___ ___

```
S  S  E  N  E  L  T  N  E  G  S  L  I
P  S  P  A  T  I  E  N  C  E  S  O  R
N  S  E  A  W  V  P  J  F  V  E  V  O
P  V  Y  N  N  X  J  S  X  Z  N  E  V
I  E  D  Q  D  O  I  W  P  B  K  V  B
F  A  A  O  Y  N  I  N  S  B  E  O  I
I  J  P  C  S  Z  I  M  I  H  E  Z  M
O  I  W  X  E  I  F  K  X  Z  M  U  B
```

TESTIMONY

How do we receive a testimony of The Book of Mormon? Decode the important scripture below to find the answer.

"And when ye shall receive these things, I would exhort you that ye would

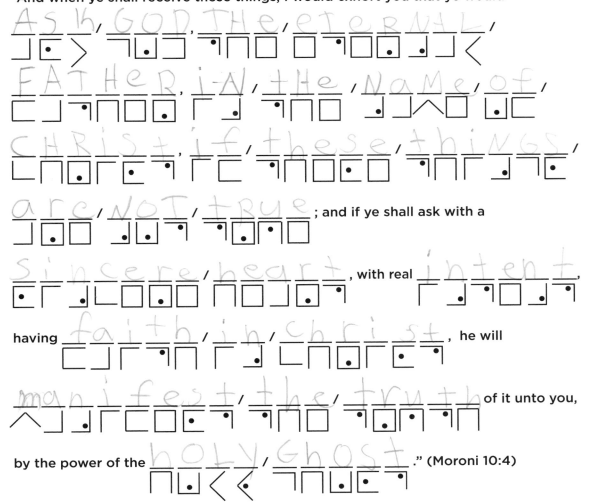

ASK, GOD, THE, ETERNAL,

FATHER, IN, the, NaMe, of,

CHRIST, if, these, things,

are, NOT, true; and if ye shall ask with a

Sincere, heart, with real intent,

having faith, in, Christ, he will

manifest, the, truth of it unto you,

by the power of the HOLY, GhOST." (Moroni 10:4)

ONE MAN'S MIRACLE

Jesus performed many miracles while on the earth. In a New Testament story, he raises a man from the dead. To find out the name of this man, write the answers in the boxes next to each clue. The highlighted boxes will tell you his name. Then read the story in John 11:1–44.

1. This fruit looks like a lemon, but it is green.
2. This is a very dark color, dark as night.
3. If you don't do very much, what are you called?
4. A long time ago, kings and queens lived in these.
5. This type of car can carry a lot of stuff in the back.
6. When you do something fast, what can you be called?
7. When you clean, what do you do to tables and pictures?

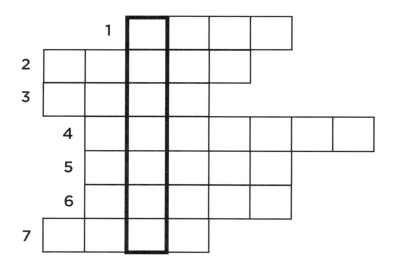

PUZZLE THAT!

Moroni tells us of some important things that will help lead to our salvation. To find out what these things are, collect all the letters with the numbers 1 and write them in order on the first line. Do the same for the numbers 2–10.

R	L	H	M	E	E	H	G	T	E
2	4	6	3	8	10	5	7	9	3
F	O	N	E	N	E	O	E	L	W
1	4	10	5	8	2	6	3	6	4
A	D	P	H	A	E	N	R	K	Y
1	8	2	9	5	2	2	5	3	6
T	L	I	H	U	E	R	O	N	I
2	4	1	7	8	9	8	7	3	4
D	N	A	E	N	S	T	I	T	E
10	4	2	4	2	7	5	8	1	3
N	S	G	S	T	C	E	H	S	S
8	3	8	4	7	2	2	1	4	3

__ __ __ __ __ , __ __ __ __ __ __ __ __ __ __ __ ,

_____1_____ _____2_____

__ __ __ __ __ __ __ __ , and __ __ __ __ __ __ __ __ __ of

_____3_____ _____4_____

__ __ __ __ __ , receiving the __ __ __ __ __ __ __ __ __ ,

____5____ ____6____ ____7____

and __ __ __ __ __ __ __ to __ __ __ __ __ __ .

_____8_____ ___9___ ___10___

Moroni 8:25–26

BLESSINGS OF FAITH

Read each scripture below and use the clues to unscramble the words. Place the circled letters in order in the spaces at the bottom to find what faith in Christ can bring us.

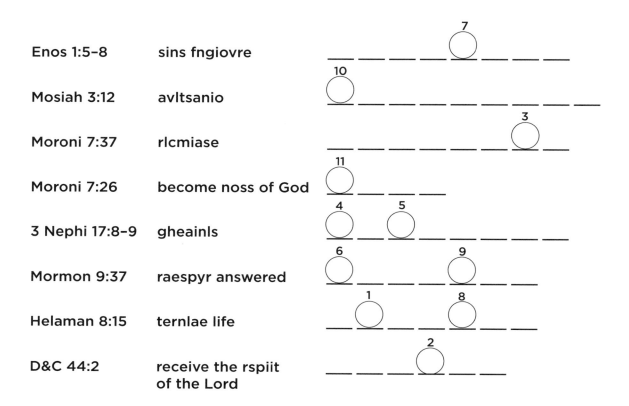

Enos 1:5–8   sins fngiovre

Mosiah 3:12   avltsanio

Moroni 7:37   rlcmiase

Moroni 7:26   become noss of God

3 Nephi 17:8–9   gheainls

Mormon 9:37   raespyr answered

Helaman 8:15   ternlae life

D&C 44:2   receive the rspiit
                    of the Lord

___ ___ u ___   ___ ___ P ___ ___ ___ ___ ___
 1   2   3   4   5   6   7   8   9 10 11

PICTURE SEARCH

In the picture of Moses parting the Red Sea, there are many items hidden. Find a book, a pan, a bird, a hammer, a vest, a sword, a shovel, a cup, and a hat. Then read Exodus 14:21.

WHICH ONE AM I?

Use the table to find which letter belongs in the blanks to decode this Article of Faith.

	1	2	3	4	5	6	7	8	9
A	I	S	A	R	N	H	B	L	S
B	F	M	O	P	E	M	W	K	V
C	R	N	I	D	C	Y	O	T	G
D	O	G	H	L	S	I	E	S	R
E	A	W	O	T	D	N	R	U	X

"We believe ___ ___ ___ ___   ___ ___ ___ ___ ___ ___ ___   ___ ___ ___
                C8 D3 A3 E4   C8 D3 E7 D1 E8 D2 A6   E4 D3 D7

___ ___ ___ ___ ___ ___ ___ ___ ___   ___ ___   ___ ___ ___ ___ ___ ___
A3 E4 E3 C2 D7 B2 D7 E6 C8   C7 B1   C5 D3 A4 D6 D8 E4

___ ___ ___   ___ ___ ___ ___ ___ ___ ___   ___ ___ ___   ___ ___
A3 A8 D4   B2 E1 E6 B8 C3 E6 C4   B2 A3 C6   A7 B5

___ ___ ___ ___ ___,   ___ ___   ___ ___ ___ ___ ___ ___ ___ ___ ___
D5 E1 B9 B5 C4   A7 C6   C7 A7 B5 C4 A1 B5 E6 C5 D7

___ ___   ___ ___ ___   ___ ___ ___ ___   ___ ___ ___
E4 D1   E4 D3 B5   D4 A3 B7 D5   A3 E6 C4

___ ___ ___ ___ ___ ___ ___ ___ ___ ___   ___ ___   ___ ___ ___
D1 C1 C4 A1 C2 A3 E6 C5 B5 D8   C7 B1   E4 D3 B5

___ ___ ___ ___ ___ ___."
C9 C7 A9 B4 B5 D4

NAME THAT WORD!

When we are baptized we are making a commitment with Heavenly Father to be obedient to him by keeping his commandments. To find out what this commitment is called, connect the dots to spell the word.

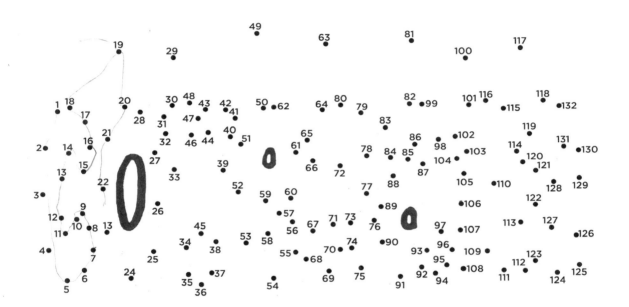

GUESS WHO?

In the Old Testament, a fisherman was called to be an apostle. This man testified of Christ, then denied knowing him 3 times. To find the name of this apostle, write the answer to each clue in the matching line of the acrostic puzzle. The shaded area will reveal his name. If you get stuck, look up Matthew 4:18-20.

1. This is an animal that has gills and lives under water.
2. What does a fish have that helps it swim?
3. Fish do this in the water to get from one place to another
4. When you go fishing, you can sit in one of these on the water.
5. You use this to carry a fish after you catch it.
6. You use a fishing _____ to catch fish.
7. These type of birds fly all around the beach near the ocean.
8. The ocean is a big body of _____.
9. After you cook a fish you can _____ it.
10. This is what you use to bait your fishing hook.

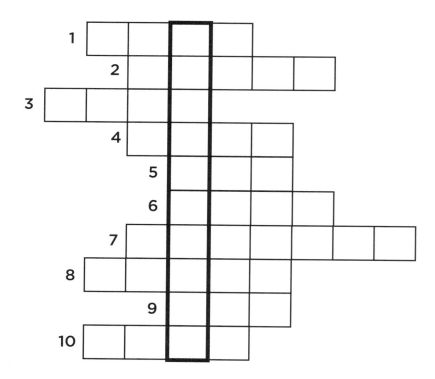

THE LORD'S DIRECTION

Heavenly Father gave Lehi and Nephi a compass in the wilderness to help them find their way. What was the name of the compass? Cross out every letter that appears 4 times. Then write the remaining letters in order in the spaces below to find out.

```
B  X  J  C  M  L  F  P  Z
I  R  S  A  S  T  B  J  U
K  D  C  J  R  M  Z  S  H
F  O  P  X  U  F  T  D  B
Z  U  T  K  N  S  X  M  C
T  D  F  J  B  K  R  P  X
P  K  M  Z  D  R  C  U  A
```

___ ___ ___ ___ ___ ___ ___

(See Alma 37:38.)

ARTICLES OF FAITH

Use your knowledge of the Articles of Faith to solve the crossword puzzle. If you need help, look them up!

ACROSS:

5. We believe in the gift of _____.

7. We are _____ by immersion.

8. We honor, obey, and sustain the _____.

10. He will reign during the millennium.

DOWN:

1. Word #5 in the 13th Article of Faith.

2. This is the New Jerusalem.

3. We seek anything _____.

4. We will not be punished for the fall of _____.

6. The literal gathering of _____.

9. We believe in the freedom of _____.

PICTURE SEARCH

There are many items hidden in the picture of Lehi. Find a shoe, a bone, a comb, a book, a bird, a glove, a candle, and a fish.

FREEDOM OF RELIGION

Which Article of Faith are these words from? Find them in the word search to reveal the hidden answer.

```
P W H E R E E L E E S V E
I W N T H D A G R A T I C
H H L E O O E F M F A I T
S A L G H L L E W K X S L
R T B E I Y T H G I M L A
O F I V T F D C R K Z H D
W G I E V B W E L Z B W O
W R D N B V Z B L X I O W
P K V N M R B S K Q M W N
```

ALMIGHTY

OWN

WHAT

GOD

PRIVILEGE

WHERE

LET

SAME

WORSHIP

__ __ __ __ __ __ __ __   __ __ __ __ __ __

__ __ __ __ __ __ __

VANISHED VOWELS

Words from the 10th Article of Faith are missing vowels. Replace the vowels with the ones listed below. Each of the letters will be used only once so make sure to cross each one off as you use it.

A A A E E E E E E E E E I I I I I I I I O O O O O Y

1. ___SR___ ___L

2. T___N TR___B___S

3. R___ST___R___T___ ___N

4. G___TH___R___NG

5. R___N___W___D

6. CHR___ST

7. GL___R___

8. Z___ ___N

9. C___NT___N___NT

10. R___ ___GN

AN ANGEL VISITS

The angel Moroni appeared to Joseph Smith to tell him about the gold plates. See if you can draw the angel Moroni on the next page.

HIDING HYMN

What hymn are these words from? Find them in the word search, then write the first unused letters in the blanks until they are full to find out which hymn they come from!

```
S R E C I O H C B P C H O O S
H E H O L Y E E L T T H E R I
I V G H T Y F A J T I L W I C
N E C A T O C L J N H R S Y U
I R Y V R E V L Z D E D I B C
N O Y E D B W I V L T F Z P L
G F X J Z V I G N F H P W Y S
P S G A W R S H D M G M X M I
N O H T Y L D T M B I S F I J
I V F R R H O L E Y R Q J V X
A U J M F P M A N J R F R X D
X W U L M R V I Y B O P B N D
```

BEFORE	CHOICE	FOREVER
HOLY	LIGHT	PLACED
RIGHT	SHINING	SPIRIT
WISDOM		

__ __ __ __ __ __ __ __ __ __ __ __ __ __

A MIRACULOUS BATTLE

There was a man in the Book of Mormon that had 2,000 adopted sons that were brave, obedient, and disciplined. All 2,000 of them fought and survived battles. To find out the name of this man, write the names of the pictures in the matching line of the acrostic puzzle. The shaded area will tell you his name.

1.

2.

3.

4.

5.

6.

7.

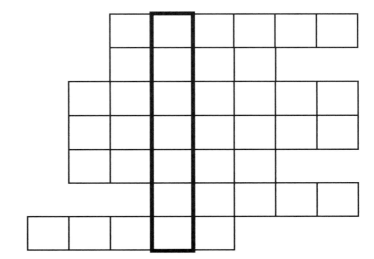

LIVING A REVERENT LIFE

Unscramble the words in the left column and write them in the blanks in the right column. Then place the numbered letters in their corresponding spaces below to find out what these things help us become.

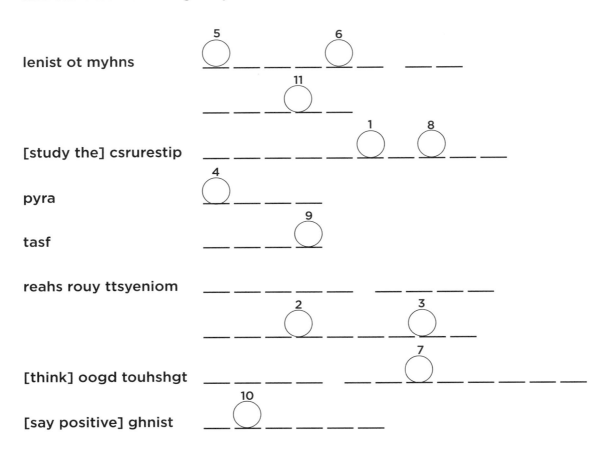

lenist ot myhns

[study the] csrurestip

pyra

tasf

reahs rouy ttsyeniom

[think] oogd touhshgt

[say positive] ghnist

We do these things to help us become:

__ __ __ __ __ __ W __ __ __ __ __
1 2 3 4 5 6   7 8 9 10 11

THE BOOKS IN THE BOOK OF MORMON

Complete the crossword puzzle by solving the clues about the names of the books. Do not include the numbers when you are putting the names in the puzzle.

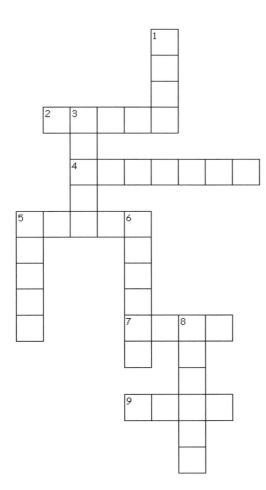

ACROSS:

2. This is the 1st book in the Book of Mormon.
4. This book has the 2nd longest name.
5. You could spell "major" with the letters in this name.
7. This is the 9th book.
9. You could spell "nose" with the letters in this book.

Down:

1. This book has an "m" and "n" in the middle of its name.
3. This is the 2nd to last book.
5. This is a common boy's name.
6. This is the 8th book in the Book of Mormon.
8. This book has an "i" and an "r" in its name.

HEART FELT WORDS

Starting with the letter "L" at the top center of the heart, write the letter in the first blank below. Going left, skip a letter and write the next letter on the next blank, skip another letter and so on. Cross out each letter as you use it. When you reach the end of the circles, go back to the beginning and write the letters you have not used yet in order to fill in the rest of the blanks.

Malachi prophesied that in the ___ ___ ___ ___ ___ ___ days Elijah

would "turn the ___ ___ ___ ___ ___ of the ___ ___ ___ ___ ___ ___ ___

to the ___ ___ ___ ___ ___ ___ ___ ___, and the ___ ___ ___ ___ ___

of the ___ ___ ___ ___ ___ ___ ___ ___ to their

___ ___ ___ ___ ___ ___ ___."

Malachi 4:5–6

JOSEPH FIELDING SMITH

Decode the quote by the prophet Joseph Fielding Smith.

A	B	C	D	E	F	G	H	I	J	K	L	M	N	O	P	Q	R	S	T
			15	17				1				7		16	2			18	

U	V	W	X	Y	Z

"O __ __   M I S S I O __   I S   __ O
16 6 12   7 1 18 18 1 16 14   1 18   20 16

P __ E __ __ __   __ __ E   __ D O __ __ __ I __ E S
2 12 17 3 13 22   20 22 17   15 16 13 20 12 1 14 17 18

O __   S __ __ __ __ __ I O __   I __
16 26   18 3 19 9 3 20 1 16 14   1 14

P __ __ I __ __ E S S   __ __ D
2 19 3 1 14 14 17 18 18   3 14 15

S I M P __ I __ I __ __   __ S   __ __ E __
18 1 7 2 19 1 13 1 20 5   3 18   20 22 17 5

__ __ E   __ E __ E __ __ E D   __ __ D
3 12 17   12 17 9 17 3 19 17 15   3 14 15

__ E __ O __ D E D I __ __ __ E
12 17 13 16 12 15 17 15   1 14   20 22 17

S __ __ I P __ __ __ E S ."
18 13 12 1 2 20 6 12 17 18

GREAT PROPHETS

Unscramble the names of the latter-day prophets below. Then copy the letters in the numbered cells to spaces with the same number to discover who the prophet at the bottom of the page was.

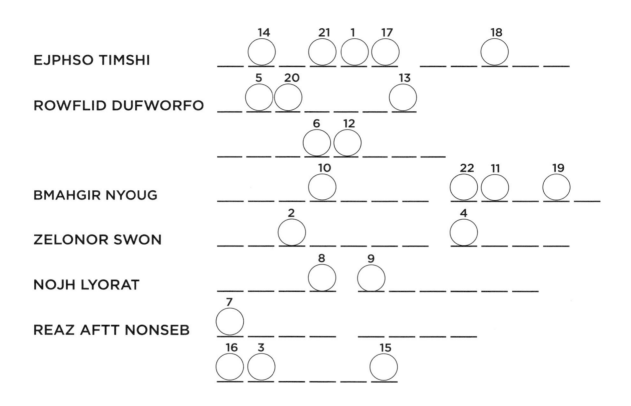

EJPHSO TIMSHI

ROWFLID DUFWORFO

BMAHGIR NYOUG

ZELONOR SWON

NOJH LYORAT

REAZ AFTT NONSEB

This man was the prophet when the 100th temple was built.

___ ___ ___ ___ ___ ___ ___ ___ ___   ___ ___ ___ ___ ___ ___
1   2   3   4   5   6   7   8   9   10 11 12 13 14 15

___   ___ ___ ___   K ___ ___ ___
16   17 18 19   20 21 22

THE LIGHT INSIDE

Put the correct letter in the blanks below by using the key given.

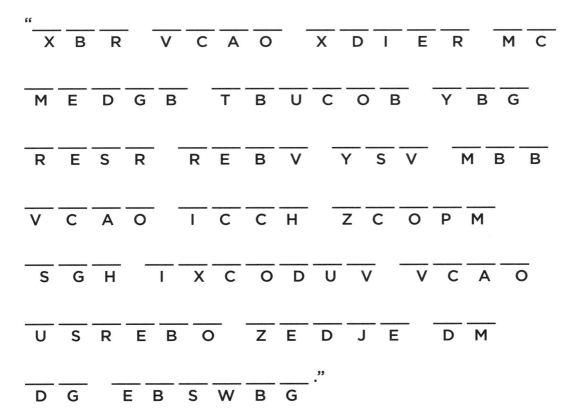

```
A=U    B=E    C=O    D=I
E=H    G=N    H=D    I=G
J=C    K=P    M=S    O=R
P=K    R=T    S=A    T=B
U=F    V=Y    W=V    X=L
Y=M    Z=W
```

" LET YOUR LIGHT SO
X B R   V C A O   X D I E R   M C

SHINE BEFORE MEN
M E D G B   T B U C O B   Y B G

THAT THEY MAY SEE
R E S R   R E B V   Y S V   M B B

YOUR GOOD WORKS
V C A O   I C C H   Z C O P M

AND GLORIFY YOUR
S G H   I X C O D U V   V C A O

FATHER WHICH IS
U S R E B O   Z E D J E   D M

IN HEAVEN."
D G   E B S W B G

MATTHEW 5:16
Y S R R E B Z

OBEDIENCE

Read Luke 22:33–39. Christ willingly gave his live for us in obedience to the Father's will. We must also be obedient to Heavenly Father and Jesus Christ. Using the shapes below, fill in each blank with the corresponding letter for that shape. Then unscramble the important message that tells us what we show to the Lord when we are obedient.

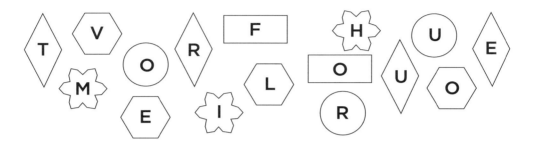

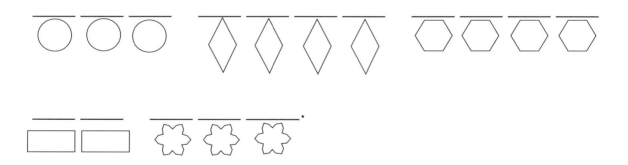

LEARNING TRUTH

Find the words in the word search. Then write the first unused letters in the blanks until all the blanks are full to reveal a hidden message.

```
S   S   E   N   I   P   P   A   H   I   K   N   P
M   O   D   S   I   W   F   O   D   R   O   W   R
Y   S   U   O   E   T   H   G   I   R   L   E   O
E   T   L   O   R   D   P   O   W   T   A   V   M
S   H   I   A   T   E   M   Y   H   E   N   R   I
O   E   A   R   A   V   E   N   L   Y   R   E   S
O   F   V   C   A   A   T   H   E   R   E   S   E
H   L   E   O   O   H   O   N   E   S   T   Y   S
C   V   E   S   L   M   C   E   Q   B   E   U   H
```

CHARITY   CHOOSE   ETERNAL
HAPPINESS   HONESTY   LORD
LOVE   PEACE   PROMISES
RIGHTEOUS   SERVE   WORD OF WISDOM

__ / __ __ __ __ / __ __ __ __ / __ __

__ __ __ __ __ __ __ __ / __ __ __ __ __ __

__ __ __ __ __ / __ __.

A WONDERFUL GIFT

Who are each of these clues describing? Read each of the scriptures listed for clues to unscramble each word or phrase. Then fill in the last clue to find out!

- Helaman 5:45–47
- 1 Nephi 10:17
- 2 Nephi 32:8

- Moroni 10:8
- Moroni 8:26
- Moroni 10:5

VSSOINI

TUHTR OF LAL SINHTG

ROTCOMFER

SIFTG FO HET TSPIIR

LESGEFNI FO EPCAE

CATHEES SU TO RYAP

____ ____ ____ ____ / ____ ____ ____ ____ ____
1   2   3   4   5   6   7   8   9

PARABLES

Why did Jesus speak in parables? Decode the underlined words in the scripture below using the chart to fill in each letter to find out.

	C	H	R	I	S	T
1	A	P	K	L	B	S
2	X	I	D	W	H	D
3	G	J	L	F	U	C
4	T	N	S	O	R	A
5	Q	Y	K	G	M	T
6	E	Z	V	B	X	Y

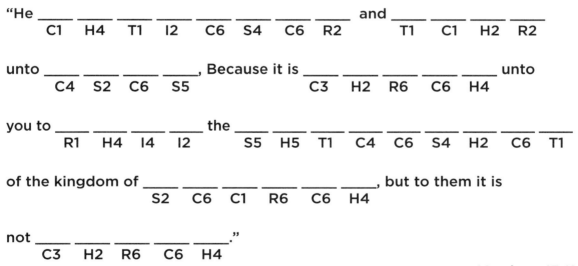

"He ____ ____ ____ ____ ____ ____ ____ and ____ ____ ____ ____
   C1 H4 T1 I2 C6 S4 C6 R2   T1 C1 H2 R2

unto ____ ____ ____ ____, Because it is ____ ____ ____ ____ ____ unto
   C4 S2 C6 S5   C3 H2 R6 C6 H4

you to ____ ____ ____ ____ the ____ ____ ____ ____ ____ ____ ____ ____
   R1 H4 I4 I2   S5 H5 T1 C4 C6 S4 H2 C6 T1

of the kingdom of ____ ____ ____ ____ ____ ____, but to them it is
   S2 C6 C1 R6 C6 H4

not ____ ____ ____ ____ ____."
   C3 H2 R6 C6 H4

Matthew 13:11

Leatherwood Press books are available exclusively
through Deseret Book Distributors.

For details, write or telephone:
Deseret Book Distributors, 40 East South Temple
Salt Lake City, Utah 84111, (801) 534-1515

Leatherwood Press LLC
8160 South Highland Drive
Sandy, Utah 84093
www.leatherwoodpress.com

Copyright © 2006 by Leatherwood Press LLC
All rights reserved. This book, or parts thereof, may
not be reproduced in any form without permission.
ISBN 978-1-59992-005-4

Reprinted in the United States 2007